PUTTING THE SOUL BACK IN MEDICINE

Reflections on Compassion and Ethics

David Schiedermayer, M.D.

Baker Books

A Division of Baker Book House Co
Grand Rapids, Michigan 49516

Published by Baker Books
a division of Baker Book House Company
P.O. Box 6287, Grand Rapids, MI 49516-6287

Second printing, September 1994

Printed in the United States of America

Library of Congress Cataloging-in-Publication Data

Schiedermayer, David L.
    Putting the soul back in medicine : reflections on medical ethics /
    David Schiedermayer.
        p.   m.
    Includes bibliographical references.
    ISBN 0-8010-8374-5
    1. Medical ethics—Religious aspects. 2. Medical care—Religious
aspects. I. Title.
    R725.55.S37 1994
    241'.642—dc20

For
my mother and father
with love

Contents

Part Four **Overcoming the World**

Acknowledgments

This book has been over ten years in the writing, and credit for some of its contents goes to the late Sid Macauley, former editor of the *Christian Medical & Dental Society Journal*, who believed in the importance of medical ethics. His work has been continued by Dave Biebel, my friend and current director of publications for CMDS, who had a heart for this book and kept calling me until I completed the project. Hal Habecker has encouraged me all along the way, and Juanita McGinnis kept me on deadline over the years. My editor, Betty De Vries, treated the manuscript like a baby: with love, but often in need of changes.

My family put up with the long hours I spent studying ethics and medicine, and a move to Chicago to spend a year in full-time research and writing. I'd like to acknowledge my family for the special place each one has in my life: my parents, Larry and Audrey Schiedermayer, for giving me life and hope; my brother Brett Schiedermayer and his wife Clare, for helping me to love a simple life and for hospitality in New York; Arnie and Mabe Grummer, for having Kim and for early inspiration in writing; Greg Grummer for his poetic voice and for editing early versions of "Cardinal Jackson"; Mark Grummer, for inspiration in running and photographs of our family; Jarv and Monie Mattes and family, for their example of faith and long-time shepherding; Jan and Gene Schiedermayer and family, for their love of nature and of wild horses; Pete and Phelan Femal and family, for celebrating

Long Lake summers with us; and Grandma Molly Schiedermayer, for her outlandish humor, love of books, and her
warm, hand-knitted comforters.

Mark Seversen and John Mackett, pastor and associate
pastor of Meadowbrook Church, have been colleagues in
ministry.

Finally, I'd like to thank Bob and Win Couchman for spiritual mentoring over the years, and Ron and Edie Miller for
early and continual prayer support. Doctors are often stub-
born, solitary creatures who refuse to believe in anyone but
themselves and maybe their own families, and maybe God.
The Couchmans and the Millers have taught me that spiritual friends can be forever family too.

Introduction

Mrs. Anna Velosian's daughter calls me to say the cancer on her mother's neck is bleeding heavily. I leave my office to make the house call on the eighty-eight-year-old Armenian woman. Her daughter meets me in the kitchen, and her mother is sitting on the sofa. Mrs. Velosian stands to greet me; she is four feet eight and now weighs eighty-five pounds. Ten years ago she decided that she didn't want us to treat the slow-growing cancer on her thyroid. But Mrs. Velosian's cancer has recently transformed into an anaplastic tumor, and now is the size of a billiard ball. I remove the bandage and see that the white, glistening tumor has grown right through the skin. There is a red, open patch the size of a quarter. There are no visible bleeding vessels. Mrs. Velosian's daughter shows me the bedroom. Blood stains the pillows, the sheets, even the mattress. I return to Mrs. Velosian. She gives me a big smile.

"How are you?" I ask.

She is hard of hearing, but she knows what to say. She always says the same thing to her doctor. "Fine," she says. "Fine." And I see the cross on her wall and I remember her life story and I think, yes, you will be fine. You are fine now and you will be finer. I call the home hospice nurse and I tell

An adapted version of this material appeared in the October 4, 1993 issue of *Christianity Today*.

the daughter to call the relatives, because it will not be long now and Mrs. Anna Velosian will be going home to be with Jesus.

Mr. Albert Tsosie is a Navajo man who is dying of diabetic kidney disease. He has been on dialysis, but he has developed an abdominal infection. His heart is failing. His wife and sister are at his bedside. I am writing notes in the nurses' station of the small hospital on the Navajo reservation. I will return to his room in a few minutes, I think, and I will find him dead. But I am wrong. I enter the room just as he is taking his last breath. I am there to witness. He has been going downhill for days, his serum chemistries rising, his vital signs slipping. Now as I stand in the doorway to his room I think death has moved in just ahead of me, sliding past me through the door. The Navajo man's eyes are turned away. The room is still. Death moves, pulling him away. I turn toward his family. I begin to speak of his disease and his death. But even as I try to talk to Mr. Tsosie's wife and sister, I see an amazing thing. At the moment they perceive his death they physically turn away from him in horror and fear. And they will not speak of him again. For the traditional Navajo, death is the ultimate void.

Mrs. Iona Christiansen had suffered anoxic encephalopathy (brain damage) from a cardiac arrest and was being cared for by her husband at home. He washed, turned, and fed her. He did have home health aides coming to assist him daily, but the brunt of the care fell on him. Mr. Christiansen felt good about his new role, reasoning that during his working life his wife cared for their children with little help from him, and now he was returning the favor. He had been taking care of her for about a year when I began making house calls. The house calls were clinically indicated because he had to call an ambulance for transport and because Mrs. Christiansen could not sit up for more than short periods.

Mrs. Christiansen could follow me with her eyes, but she was unable to communicate. She did not require tube feeding, but her meals were long and laborious. Sometimes Mr. Christiansen or the aide would take over an hour to feed her. A year passed. Feeding became more difficult. It became clear that Mrs. Christiansen was dying.

On a Thursday morning, her breathing became irregular. Mr. Christiansen sounded frightened on the phone. I left the clinic (office in which I saw patients), went over to the house, and spent some time. Nothing more could be done for his wife; she was not in pain and she was dying peacefully. I gave Mr. Christiansen a hug. His wife died three hours later. I went back to write the official pronouncement of her death. I went to the funeral and heard the testimony of her love for God and for life before she was stricken.

Sitting in the back, I thought of all the lessons I had learned from my patients over the years. They have taught me much about death—and life—just by allowing me the privilege of observing them at the end. Whether you are a doctor, a nurse, an allied health professional, or you have an illness yourself or have a loved one who is ill, you have probably already thought about these lessons. Much of this book focuses on these lessons, but let me begin with them here.

Lesson One: Life has a tenacious, innate dignity.

The dignity of life is an inner, God-given grace which projects out toward the doctor, so that despite the cynicism with which we guard ourselves, we are taken aback. The Down syndrome child has dignity. The patient with Alzheimer's disease has dignity. The child has dignity, the elderly person has dignity, and if we look at the ultrasound, the unborn baby has dignity. The Scripture in Isaiah 46:3–5 says, "Listen to me, O house of Jacob, all you who remain of the house of Israel, you whom I have upheld since you were conceived, and have carried since your birth. Even to your old age and gray hairs I am he, I am he who will sustain you. I have made you and I will carry you; I will sustain you and I will rescue you." So patients have dignity, patients like Mrs. Velosian, Mr. Tsosie, Mrs. Christiansen. One can't take the dignity away from life. It is innate. God gives it. The dignity of life is surprisingly strong and sustained, and is intertwined with life itself.

Lesson Two: Christians are not promised eternal life in the biological sphere.

Even though we value life we are not obligated to endlessly prolong human life here on earth. Mrs. Velosian has refused aggressive treatment for her cancer, and she has lived many trouble-free years until it began to grow wildly. Now the cancer will take her life, but she will die at home. Mrs. Christiansen received aggressive supportive care at home, but died despite all the loving ministrations of her husband. Honoring life does not mean we must insist on all forms of treatment for all people at all times. That is honoring technology. That is the technological imperative. God is sovereign and he determines the span of our lives. The Christian is not granted eternal life in the biological sphere.

When a doctor writes a patient's phone number on a chart it is not just so he or she can call to tell the patient the lab results or so the office can bug a patient about missing appointments or paying bills (so we can make our boat payments). Sometimes doctors have to use phone numbers to call with bad news. We are sorry about that, but it just proves that doctors can't play God very well (though we try), but God can play a doctor perfectly. God is the only one who can really give eternal life.

Lesson Three: We are not thankful or grateful enough for life and we do not fear death enough.

God has given life dignity, and he has made us tenacious, but death is just a breath away. We can learn from the traditional Navajos, who like many spiritual people realize that, without Christ and the hope of an afterlife, death is to be greatly feared. The traditional Navajo knows enough to turn away from the dead in horror, even a family member like Mr. Tsosie. Why? Because life is good and death is bad. When I treat patients and they get better, when their heart disease or hypertension or stroke or cancer gets a little better, I am happy for them. But I am never flippant. Because death will beat me. Death beats every doctor, and it drives us wild, it makes us crazy. Death is always going into Mr. Tsosie's room just ahead of me, always stealing the victory from me. So be it. The Scriptures tell us that Christ, not the doctor, has conquered death.

Lesson Four: We have no right to procrastinate with our lives because we do not own them.

We as Christians are like the man whose doctor called him and said, "I have bad news for you." "What's the news?" the man said. "Well," the doctor said, "you have twenty-four hours to live." "That is bad news," the man said. "I have even worse news," the doctor said. "What could be worse than that?" the man asked. "Well, I tried to call you yesterday." This is a modern retelling of Jesus' parable about the rich man who was going to build bigger barns, but God called him and said, "I have bad news." This is also the bottom line of Ecclesiastes 12:1–6, where we are told to honor God in the days of our youth.

Because life is dignified, we prepare for its passing. And when life ends, we marvel at its passing, and we look up to God, who gave it so miraculously and received it back so mysteriously, and we ought to say, "God, I believe, help my unbelief."

I stir at the back of the church, at the end of the funeral. I think I will slip out quietly now, finished with my funeral charting, my musing, my elegy of life. I expect to find death outside, but again I am wrong. God has gone ahead of me, as he goes on ahead of each of us if we will. And when I step through the door, the sun shines brightly. The air moves with a fresh wind. The day is full of promise. I am alive.

Part One

Caring for Body, Mind, and Soul

1

The Heart Man

A road winds down from Kpayerkolli toward the sea, and
in the dry season it is a road of red dust. In West Africa,
where the villages are small and scattered in the bush, Kpayerkolli is just one of many such villages, and if you do not
go with someone who knows it, you will never find it. If you
walk there, you will be coated with dust; it will sift into your
ears and eyes and cover your clothes.

The road is always full of people, especially children, since
there are so many of them. A road means freedom to walk,
freedom from poisonous snakes and from the rough jungle
terrain. If you talk to the children on the road, they will shyly
say they are glad to meet you, that they are well (even if they
are not), and that they are going to school soon. They will
not tell you about the Heart Man.

You will see them come to the point where the road goes
on and the little path turns off toward their village, and they
will run wildly off the road and down the path. When you
ask why, they will not tell you. Only when they are older,
and when you are their friend, will they tell you. It is not in
any book.

19

The reason they run, they explain, is that there is a Heart Man from a big city. He comes out to the villages where there are many children. He likes young hearts because they are tender and full of life. He looks for children coming off the road, and when he catches one he takes the heart right out, still beating, for his own use. One little child is gone and nothing can be done, for the Heart Man disappears. That is why the children run fast when they come off the road, and why they grease their bodies to make them slippery.

What has this to do with doctors? We are highly educated professionals, not little children running through the bush. But we are in grave danger from the Heart Man, who is in every culture in a different form. He is after our hearts.

Our road is the superhighway, and we live in the fast lane. We cannot travel there unless we are really moving. We suffer from this pace. Physicians state that the lack of time is their number-one dissatisfaction. Large numbers of patients, heavy on-call schedules, reading, teaching, and research all take up professional time. There are many things to look at besides the patient. From the patient's viewpoint this may be seen as a loss of compassion, but sometimes it is just life on the highway; we have to look at the laboratory results and scans as we whiz by the patient. Time is a Heart Man after our hearts, and he wants to drive us faster and faster, until we go right past all for which we should stop. And the Heart Man lies in wait to ensnare all who provide health care: More patients, work faster, learn new technology, be cost-effective, be always available and hyper-responsible, make no errors, work longer shifts, staff cuts coming, more paper work, be sure to smile. This Heart Man also goes after our personal lives, until we neglect ourselves and our families.

We doctors travel down our road repetitively, and it can bore and irritate us. We see the chronically ill over and over again. Sometimes they are helpless victims, but sometimes, with cigarettes and alcohol, they foreshadow their own demise. Our scientific knowledge is impressive, but there are still many things we cannot cure. And it frustrates us to see certain patients return again and again. All these things can harden our hearts and steal them from their true purpose, which is to feel compassion.

Our road has more signs than the one in West Africa. There are so many signs they may also distract us.

One sign is the dollar sign. It is a necessary sign but all too easy to focus on. We feel it is our right to earn money in keeping with our education and experience. No one disputes that our education has monetary value or that we have accrued large debts. But the Heart Man is lurking behind the dollar sign, and he loves to get us and squeeze the good motivation out of us until he has in his hands a greedy little heart.

Another sign is the one-way sign. We endure long years of training, which include alternatively ego buffeting and ego building, and we become professionals. Eventually we feel that we are different, maybe even better, than others. We may start to see things only one way—our way. But the Heart Man is stealing our hearts, and if he is not stopped, all that will be left is an empty, self-seeking space.

One scene on our road we too often forget is the scene of an accident. We are unaware that the Heart Man causes the accidents, even though we may witness them on our own road. At the scene of the accident we see colleagues who have lost their hearts, and on occasion their lives. Drug abuse, alcoholism, and suicide result in the loss of seven hundred physicians per year in the United States—several entire medical school classes. We travel by and think it could never happen to us, but it could next time, next year, or next decade.

In varying degrees, and with perhaps fewer statistics to show, all health-care givers are vulnerable prey to the Heart Man in one of his guises. From the doctor in training to the nurses and technicians to the nursing home aides to family members—all have their source of stress and temptations, and for countless people that breaking point looms ever nearer.

With God's help, we need to keep our hearts young and tender and not let the demands of time, frustration, love of money, or selfishness steal them from us. We need to acknowledge our vulnerability to the Heart Man who comes in these and other guises to change our hearts and take them away from us. We need to run away from him when he comes, run hard and fast, until we come at last to our own village.

2

House Calls on Cardinal Jackson

House calls are easily scheduled. You look on your pocket calendar for a time when you are not in meetings or in clinic. Over the lunch hour, maybe. You call the person you are going to see, tell him or her of your plans, then see if he or she agrees. You don't even need a secretary to make the arrangements for you. Like a rendezvous with a friend, a house call is something you'd best plan yourself. And don't forget to ask for directions.

I began visiting Cardinal Jackson when she was seventy-three. Now she's seventy-nine. She lives in the central city of Milwaukee. If you take 27th Street north from Wisconsin Avenue, you pass Family Hospital, now out of business. You pass the businessmen cruising for prostitutes on State. You pass the porn shops, the pawn shops, the checks-cashed shops, and you turn and finally arrive at a neighborhood where a large factory provides several hundred decent jobs. Around this factory, neat little green-lawned homes prove that jobs mean life and love. Some of the homes have chain-link fences with gates in front of them. Cardinal's home has such a fence, with a little latch on the gate that you have to lift up. No drug houses on her street, but more people hanging around the corners than a suburban doc is used to, so I fumble quickly at the latch.

My 78 Dodge Colt, golden and rusted, sits by the curb. I use it for house calls because no one ever bothers to steal it or anything in it. But even if I owned a nicer car, say a pricey little Toyota, I don't think I'd be afraid to drive it in Cardinal's neighborhood. You see, there's a factory there. Things are made near her house, heavy metal parts for engines, and Cardinal's daughter married a hard-working man. He can afford to live in this part of town.

His name is Joe Brown. I've only met him once, but I always feel his presence in the house. When I thought during one of Cardinal's hospitalizations that she was going to die, I spoke to Joe, who ran the family meeting.

"I'm sorry, really sorry to tell you all this. But we think that Cardinal is now dying. Her temperature has been over 105 for more than a day, in spite of very strong antibiotics. I'm sorry to bring you this news. We're doing all we can to keep her comfortable. She's getting Tylenol and pain medicines and she doesn't seem to be suffering from the fever."

"Doctor, when will it be? Do you know?"

"I don't know. But she can't go on like this. The fever is too high. It takes too much out of her, especially at her age. And then there is the pneumonia. It's not much better and could be getting worse."

"Thanks for calling us all here. The whole family in town is here. We will just wait. Does anyone have any questions?"

Of course, I was wrong about Cardinal. After a day or two she opened her eyes again. The fever resolved. She went home. Joe was puzzled by my deathbed predictions, I heard later from his wife. Cardinal had looked worse before.

When I walk up the steps—past neatly trimmed grass, yellow tulips, some Japanese yews—and knock on the door, it is always Cardinal's daughter who answers. Mrs. Brown was a nurse when I first met her. I agreed to see her mother at home. Six years have passed, six years of turning and wiping and washing Cardinal Jackson. Six years of house calls every month or two or three, six or seven hospitalizations for pneumonias which didn't respond to antibiotics. Always the nurse-daughter answers the door.

"Good morning, Mrs. Brown. How are you today? How is Mrs. Jackson? I haven't talked to you since we talked on the phone a while back."

"Good morning, doctor. How are you?"

"Okay, really okay. What a hot summer, eh? I think maybe I'm not dressed for it And I don't have air conditioning in my car."

"Oh, yes, it's hot. And mother feels it. She's always cool, her skin seems to stay so cool, and during the summer she heats up to about right."

"Is she still having a fever?"

"Well, only about 101 axillary."

I go to the bedside, pulling out my stethoscope. "Let's listen. Hello, Mrs. Jackson. Dr. Schiedermayer. I'm just going to listen to your lungs. Look at those braids! Who did those?"

"The kids do that. Sometimes I do. Does she sound okay?"

"Yeah, alright. But she does have the gurgles."

"Same?"

"Same, yeah. But her skin looks good. Let's look at the urine in the catheter. Looks pretty clear too, doesn't it?"

Always, when I see Cardinal Jackson, I am obsessed with her eyes. They are green, humid, warm, and smoky. Her freckles, her tiny gray braids, her smooth skin. She doesn't look a day over sixty. And she has been mindless, lights-are-on-but-nobody's-home, for over ten years. But her eyes are as wild as a girl's. They cannot say all they have seen, but that is the wonder and the mystery of Cardinal Jackson's eyes.

When she was born they named girls after birds and boys after old men. She grew up in tough times, knew hard work and poverty well enough. That is why her eyes surprise even more. You would think they would be small and cold and stony from all they had seen. But they are full as the moon, luminous and sweet.

Cardinal Jackson is always in the end of the living room. The room is set up especially for her. Mrs. Jackson's bed and medical supplies have been where they are for nearly a decade now. Occasionally the TV and sofa are moved, but the bed remains fixed. I suppose there's no other way to turn it, and if it were in the other part of the room there wouldn't be room for the sofa and the TV. I turn and speak again to Mrs. Jackson's daughter.

"The urine looks as if it is flowing all right. I don't think the fever is from a urine infection, but if we need to use antibiotics we should probably use strong ones to cover urine germs also. Do you have enough potassium?"

"Yes, I think so, but I'm going to need more Tylenol. Also, will you send the copy of the order to the home-health-care office?"

"Sure. I'll check. Now, what's happening with her skin here . . . "

"A little breakdown on mother's heel. I have a dressing on it and we are using the heel protector."

"Good; let me know if it opens up. Good; it looks like it's healing. It looks okay for now. Is she having good bowel movements?"

"Oh, yes. This new tube feeding is real good for that. Real good."

"Good. Cardinal. Cardinal! I'm going to look at your hands."

"She holds them so tight. We've got that new pad in there. If we don't use it sometimes she'll scratch herself bad right on the inside of the hand there."

"It works. This kind of protector works."

"Yeah, it's working well. I keep her nails short, too, so she won't dig them in so much like before."

"Good. I'm sorry, I can't remember now. Have we given her a flu shot every year? This year?"

"Yes. The nurse came last fall."

"Okay, we'll do it again in about two months. October. Remind me. I'll try to write it down, too. Anything else?"

"Doctor, look at this."

"Hmmm. Yes, I see that."

"What is it?"

"Well, I think just a skin growth. A skin growth, but not cancer. It comes on with aging. Has it always been that big?"

"Yes, lately."

"We'll keep an eye on it. She looks good. You have been doing a good job with her. Goodbye, Cardinal! Goodbye, Mrs. Brown."

"Goodbye, Dr. S. I'll let you out. Thank you so much for coming."

"Sure. Thank you. Call me if the fever comes back. Bye!"

The door is doubly unlocked and then doubly locked again after I leave. It's hot and miserably humid outside. A central air conditioner is humming at the side of the house.

I turn on the radio as I drive back to the hospital. I like Wisconsin Public Radio, but today they're talking about all the drive-by shootings in the inner city. The Dodge feels a bit less invincible. So I just switch over to country music. The song is about somebody's grandmother's eyes.

I drive by the factory. It's the change of shift. They still wear those blue-gray working shirts that my grandpa wore when he worked as a foreman in the paper mill. They still

carry lunches in steel buckets, probably with a small ther-
mos tucked in the upper cover. Saves the price of a cup of
coffee. I drive by the girls, the porno, the booze. I think of
Cardinal's green eyes. Somehow they help me keep driving,
keep my eyes straight ahead.

When you make house calls, an old Wisconsin doc once
told me, you should somehow find your way back to the
kitchen. The kitchen is where you learn about a patient's
personality and interests and religion. Kitchens are much
better than most rooms, especially for learning about religion. (I have had coffee in Cardinal Jackson's kitchen; it is
small but clean.)

One long glance in the fridge can be worth more than
months of futile questioning about dietary compliance in
the clinic. If a diabetic has high blood sugars, look at what
he or she eats.

Dress modestly. Carry a black bag if you have one, a
stethoscope if you don't. When you examine the patient, if
dignity permits, have a family member present. Always look
at the patient's hands and ask about his or her bowels. Talk
to both the patient and the family members.

Keep your eyes open, but don't snoop. Don't open any
drawers, but check for pets and insects and look at the art.
Remember the smell of a patient's house; let it register deep
in your brain, and you may be able to recall it when you talk
to the patient on the phone or see the patient in the office.

Maybe keep some notes. Linger just a little while longer
than you really have to. People can tell.

After making house calls to a patient, you naturally want
to go to the funeral when he or she dies. In fact, when you
make house calls you are kind of expected at the funeral.
Don't miss a one, especially in churches where the people
are so used to singing they don't use hymnals.

The old doc told me, the way things are going in medicine, doctors should make house calls whenever they can
find an excuse. I have found at least three or four.

Once you have dementia or some other seriously mind-
destroying illness, your family usually doesn't take any more
pictures of you. Even though Cardinal is beloved, this is true
of her. Her last picture was taken when she was fifty-five,
maybe sixty. Her smile is dignified. She is erect. She looks
right at you. Her hair is a bit less gray, her eyes are always
the same, but the smile says she sees the camera and knows
the photographer. She doesn't know the photographer any-
more. No use taking pictures. The lights, oh the green lights,
are on, but nobody's home, nobody's home.

When I get back to the medical school I go to my office,
which is near the anatomy lab. Sometimes I go over and sign
out the large bucket with the preserved brains in it. I give
talks at schools about the brain. The most striking thing
about the preserved brain is the heaviness. It is all dead
weight, more like an amputated limb than a brain. Lifting
it is like picking up an unexpectedly heavy stone.

The children sit enthralled at the sight and the smell of
the brain. They want me to put the brain back in the skull
I bring, but I explain that the brain is not the skull's own
brain. I see them struggle with the concept of human dissection and disembodiment. I am sympathetic; I struggle
too. What kind of person was that skull, they ask. Was it a
boy or a girl?

I can only tell them that it is good for them to take both
their brains and skulls to school. One is tempted, in school,
to use them well, even show them off a bit. Learn while you
can, I tell them. Soon enough, the brain turns to mush. And
I think of Cardinal Jackson.

Cardinal was the old kind of no-nonsense, have-fun, sing-like-an-angel Christian. Her family has been objectively blessed through it, but I wonder if they can see this as I can.

Anyway, Cardinal is now blessed. She is rocked like a baby by her daughter as if that is the normal thing to do. She is cradled, blissfully ignorant, through her slow dying and all of her leakiness. Sing it for me, the blind preacher says, when the soloist finishes the song. Sing the old song about the amazing grace of God. Please sing.

I am on the phone with Mrs. Brown. "Cardinal's fever is still there?"

"Yes, and now it's up to around 103,104. The only time it goes down is right after the Tylenol."

"Well, I guess we'll have to go with antibiotics again. Did she have diarrhea with the Keflex last time?"

"Yes, quite a bit."

"Well, let's try Cipro. Didn't that work before?"

"Yes, it knocked the fever out in two or three days. And you know, doctor, that the fever didn't come back after that one for quite a while."

"Well, let's try it. I'll call it in to the pharmacy. Is she breathing pretty fast with the fever?"

"Yes, pretty fast, and even grunting a little bit. But thanks for calling me back. And can you plan a visit a bit sooner than usual?"

"Sure. I will be there tomorrow over the noon hour. Or let's make it in the morning, around eleven."

"Okay. And can you call in some more potassium and Tylenol, too?"

"Sure I can. I don't like the rapid breathing. Keep in touch. Bye."

"Goodbye."

When I lecture, the students ask me why I keep treating her. Why not just stop treating, they ask.

Why not? Six years of knowing her, that's why not. A dozen life-threatening infections, that's why not. Already a no-code (no CPR), that's why not. Already no intensive care unit treatment, that's why not. Another doctor started the feeding, and I began caring for the patient after she had been on tube feeding for four years, that's why not. I asked the daughter several times about stopping tube feeding. Shocked her each time, and she said definitely no each time, that's why not.

A socioeconomic history of discrimination and mistreatment or undertreatment, that's why not. A tradition of poor health care and nontreatment, that's why not. The need to show her somehow we're not abandoning her, that's why not. Because her daughter's a nurse, that's why not. Because her daughter loves her and thinks it's best to keep doing things just like we are, that's why not. Because I can't stand to think of the fire dying in those green eyes, that's why not.

But why not just let her die, they ask.

And I try but I really can't explain. I can't say it. I honestly can't. It just doesn't make sense to them. They just don't understand yet, but they will understand when they have a Cardinal of their own.

Dying, you want dying, I guess I should say to them. I know how to stop treatment and let dying happen. I have stood by the bedside of plenty of patients. I have seen long, slow dying.

I have witnessed the leaving, the parting, the closing.

For example.

He has cancer of the lung but is dying of the union of the tumor's appetite with his fatigue and pain and depression. I have given him pain medication and done what I could, but he has been going downhill for the last several days, blood pressure drifting lower, pulse thready, breathing irregular. Now as I stand in his room I think that death has moved in before me, slipping in the door ahead of me.

The man's eyes are already distant. The room is cold and humming. Death has been a whispering wind in his sleep, sweeping away.

So then, I should ask the students, so then are we children of the sun or of the earth? If the students will answer this question, then I will also tell them why I don't just let Cardinal Jackson die.

What is it that gives a person dignity? What is that inner grace which projects out toward the doctor so that he, despite his intellect and education and training and skills, is taken aback? Whatever it is, Cardinal has it. And she has passed it on to her daughter. It manifests itself as inner ability, as a palpable sense of self. The dignified are above reproach.

Cardinal even moans with dignity. You can't take dignity away from the dignified. They wear it too lightly.

Once, Cardinal became critically ill in the middle of the night and the paramedics took her to the nearest hospital— not mine. Another physician took care of her, and when he called me up to tell me of his treatment plans I realized that Cardinal's disease was ordinary. To him, she looked like an old demented patient with recurrent pneumonias. He just hadn't ever seen her picture. He hadn't seen her eyes. They always close when she gets very sick. It wasn't even his fault, but he took care of her like she was a vegetable. And her family knew it. After she was discharged from the hospital, her daughter called me.

"Doctor?"

"Yes, Mrs. Brown. I heard she was in the hospital. How is she doing now? How is her breathing now?"

"She's got a bit of diarrhea from what's left of the antibiotic from the hospital. But her breathing is a lot better."

"Good. But let's try stopping the antibiotic and backing down on her tube feeding a bit. Is she still at a total of five cans a day?"

"Yes. But I've been giving her a lot of water too, because I was worried about the diarrhea."

"Well, let's back down to two cans a day, just for a day or two. But keep going with the water."

"All right."

"Is it real loose?"

"Yes, pretty much. But it is brown, and I don't see any blood."

"Good. Good. Any bedsores on her butt?"

"No, we keep her pretty well turned."

One time when I made a house call, Cardinal was so sick we had to hospitalize her emergently. I drove her daughter to the hospital. I asked her whether she ever thought about Cardinal dying.

"Oh, yes, I think about it sometimes."

"This may be the time. She's breathing fifty times a minute, and I know you don't want the respirator."

"No, no respirator. Still, God will take her when he's good and ready."

"You think soon? You mean, you think he's not going to take her this time? You think . . . "

"Well, not yet. I think she'll go more quietly, at home some night."

"Hmmm. Yes."

Cardinal does not survive because of me. She is alive because her daughter is a nurse. You can't hire love like hers. Cardinal would have been slain by a bedsore years ago if she had lived in some nursing homes. I don't know the exact cost of her care, but it's probably a lot and would be a lot more if her daughter weren't her main nurse.

The weather was turning colder. To be more specific, twelve inches of snow had fallen, and a cold sun was shining. The temperature was way below zero. I slipped through the chain-link fence and rang the doorbell.

"Hello, Mrs. Brown. What a cold day!"

"Hello, Dr. S. How are you?"

"Okay. How are you? How's Cardinal? She looks like she's resting well. And look at her hair this time!"

"Oh, she's doing pretty well, doctor. She's had a temperature of about 101, but her cough is pretty clear."

"Good. Let's see how she's doing. Her lungs sound about the same. Do you need more Tylenol?"

"Yes, I think it would be good to have some more."

"Good. Hi, Cardinal. She's really awake today. Look at these beads! How do you do this?"

"Oh, my daughter did that for Mom."

"She looks like a little girl today."

"Yes, she does." Mrs. Brown turns to a young woman who comes through the kitchen door. "Doctor S., this is my daughter, Alicia."

"Hello, Alicia. I don't think I've met you before."

"Yes, well, I've been away in the army and in school."

"Oh, what school? Far away?"

"The U."

"That's a good school. Good. What are you studying?"

"Biology."

"Oh, yeah? I studied that once or twice myself. Not always an easy topic. They can make it hard."

Mrs. Brown says proudly, "She wants to be a doctor. A pediatrician."

"Great. But it's hard. The studying is hard. They work hard. Lots of phone calls."

"I know it. But I'm doing pretty well in school."

"Well, good. I'm sure you are. Good luck. You've had plenty of practice taking care of your grandmother, here."

Both laugh. "Yes. We sure have. Yes."

Cardinal's eyes are on the ceiling. She doesn't see me when I say goodbye. But her daughter and granddaughter walk me toward the door. We talk some more about medical school. I smell Lubiderm cream. New rug. The television is on, a talk show. No change in the plaques or pictures on the walls. Something good cooking in the kitchen. I remember that smell from before: greens. Mrs. Brown unlocks the door for me, and I have time to glance back toward the bed. Cardinal Jackson is breathing slowly and steadily.

3

Honor Thy Patient

A sixty-two-year-old recently retired man who was a fore-man at a local paper mill sees his physician, complaining of abdominal pain and weight loss. He has a barium enema, and an apple core lesion highly suspicious for cancer is found in his colon. By agreement of his physician and his wife, he is not informed of the results of the x ray, and is scheduled for exploratory surgery. The cancer is found to be widespread. There are large metastatic deposits in his liver and mesentery (fat in intestines). Again, he is not informed of the findings.

He has a rapidly downhill clinical course. All of his visitors, including his eight-year-old grandson, are cautioned "not to tell" him his diagnosis. He is dead in four months.

I was the eight-year-old grandson. This man who died of colon cancer without ever officially knowing his diagnosis was my paternal grandfather. When he died in the early 1960s, many physicians withheld bad news from patients, and metastatic colon cancer is certainly bad news. There were several problems, however, with not telling my grandfather he had cancer. First, he was not given the chance to be involved (and he was the kind of man who would have wanted to be involved) in his own health care. Second, when he needed abdominal surgery, he was not really informed enough to consent to the procedure. Third, when he later became incompetent, no one knew his preferences regarding various types of treatments. His physician did not maliciously withhold the news of his cancer; on the contrary, the physician thought he was being kind and caring. He thought the information would actually harm my grandfather. "Not telling" was the standard of care until quite recently. In this chapter I will examine "not telling" in its historical and biblical contexts and in the doctor-patient relationship of the 1990s.

Informed Consent: A Brief History

Informed consent has its historical underpinnings in English common law on battery, which forbids harmful or offensive nonconsensual touching. No special exceptions were made for medical care, except in emergency situations. The modern American judicial expression of informed consent was that of Judge Cardoza in 1914: "Every human being of adult years and sound mind has a right to determine what shall be done with his own body; and a surgeon who performs an operation without his patient's consent commits an assault for which he is liable for damages."[1] A competent patient can refuse any treatment.

In the latter half of this century, the courts began to marry the provider's traditional duty to secure consent with a new affirmative obligation of disclosure, perhaps best understood as a duty to warn, resulting in a new legal doctrine of "informed consent." This doctrine was first stated in a 1957 California decision, *Salgo v. Leland Stanford, Jr., Stanford University Board of Trustees*. The judicial development of informed consent was prompted, in part, by revelations of Nazi physician atrocities during World War II and the Nuremburg Code (1946–1949) which states the "voluntary consent of the human subject is absolutely essential . . . the person involved should have sufficient knowledge and comprehension of the elements of the [experiment] involved as to enable him to make an understanding and enlightened decision [regarding participation]." The code specifies that these elements are "the nature, duration, and purpose of the experiment; the method and means by which it is to be conducted; all inconveniences and hazards reasonably to be expected; and the effects upon his health or person which may possibly come from his participation in the experiments."[2]

Some of these elements have been incorporated into the current doctrine of informed consent, which requires the doctor to discuss the following:

1. the diagnosis of the disease and prognosis if untreated
2. the treatments which might improve the prognosis
3. information on alternative treatments

Adequate informed consent involves some sort of effort on the part of the physician to assure comprehension by the patient. It is measured by the effective transfer of information that would allow reasonable persons to make prudent choices on their own behalf. It is important to note that informed consent requires far more than a signature on the bottom of a list of complications. "Such recitations," the President's Commission for the Study of Ethical Problems in Medicine and Biomedical and Behavorial Research notes, "can be so overwhelming that patients are unable to distinguish truly significant information and to make sound decisions."[3] Rather, informed consent attempts to bring a conversational imperative to the often relatively silent world of the doctor and patient.

Why Physicians Resist Informed Consent

The members of the president's commission stated that their ultimate question was, "How can a fuller, shared understanding by patient and professional of their common enterprise be promoted, so that patients can participate, on an informed basis and to the extent they care to do so, in making decisions about their health care?"[4]

Implicit in the phrasing of this question is the commission's concern that some physicians are not really obtaining "informed consent." Why have physicians so disliked the concept?

As Jay Katz, M.D., writes convincingly in his book *The Silent World of Doctor and Patient*:

Had they [physicians] appreciated that even the doctrine's [informed consent] modest appeal to patient self-determination represented a radical break with medical practices, as transmitted from teacher to student during more than two thousand years of recorded medical history, they might have been less embarrassed by standing so unpreparedly . . . before this new obligation.

They might perhaps have realized that their silence had been until most recently [the last twenty-five years] a historical necessity, dictated not only by the inadequacy of medical knowledge but also by physicians' incapacity to discriminate between therapeutic effectiveness based on their actual physical interventions, and benefits that must be ascribed to other causes. They might also have argued that the practice of silence was part of a long and venerable tradition that deserved not to be dismissed lightly. They might at least have pleaded for time, because before they could embrace the unaccustomed obligation to talk with their patients, many problems required extensive study. None of this happened. Instead, passive-aggressive defensiveness, acrimony, and confusion have marked the early history of the age of informed consent. The physician-patient dialogue, now a mixture of proffered and withheld information, has become even more opaque; surely it is not based on the idea of shared decision making.[5]

While the goal of informed consent may seem laudable, it is one which many physicians resist instinctively on several levels and for several reasons. First, as Katz notes, the idea of informed consent is a new concept, and "the art is long." Second, it is foreign to traditional medical practice and values, which are parentalistic. Third, it is a legal concept, not a medical one. As Leon Kass, M.D. puts it, "Physicians who have long taken for granted their benevolent intentions toward their patients and prided themselves on their ability to judge the just-right thing to do in the circumstances, will not see the need for, and will bridle at . . . lawyers who insist on establishing a patient's bill of rights or laying down an explicit contract between the so-called consumers and providers of health services."[6] Sider and Clements have listed the following ten problems with an informed consent, autonomy-based medical ethic:[7]

1. Such an ethic focuses on who is to choose rather than on what is chosen.
2. The assumption is that information is always a positive good and that obtaining informed consent is the physician's primary moral task.
3. The wishes of family members and physicians are considered morally irrelevant.
4. The implication is that egoism is more dependable than altruism for health care decisions.
5. The excessive emphasis on patient choice alone splits facts from values, medical science from medical ethics, and clinical thinking from moral reasoning.
6. Autonomy is considered more important than beneficence, and elaborate justifications are necessary to treat the patient for the patient's good without consent.

7. The framework assumes that a political (or legal) model is the most appropriate for the physician-patient relationship.
8. The patient preference ethic tends to confuse medical values with the individual physician's personal values.
9. The fundamental task of medical ethics in this system is to justify legal coercion.
10. Physicians risk demoralization and deprofessionalization if medical therapeutics is grounded in subjectivist preferences.

While these objections are important and have some merit, they polarize the discussion into an autonomy-beneficence dichotomy, and we are left fighting about whether the doctor or the patient knows best. This is a no-win battle; each knows *different* things. The doctor knows the diagnosis, prognosis, and treatment; the patient knows his or her preferences, pain, and suffering. In the real world, we need to talk to each other and come to a mutual understanding. We need to balance unbridled autonomy, which is perhaps better called selfishness, with the legitimate need to make one's own medical decisions as a patient. What do we know about the physician-patient dialogue?

Studies in Silence

According to Katz, while doctors and patients have always conversed, doctors have not employed words to invite patient participation in sharing the burdens of treatment decisions. As a simple illustration, he points to physicians' historical practice of silence when the patient has a fatal disease like my grandfather's, and asks, "If [physicians think] remaining life can be shortened and made insufferable by words, can it not just as easily be made insufferable by silence?"[8]

Katz's argument against silence in this setting is supported by new scientific information that patients want to know their diagnoses and prognoses even if they have fatal diseases. For example, burn patients whose survival is unprecedented and patients with inoperable cancer are not harmed by being informed of their prognoses.

Many patients also want to discuss the option of cardiopulmonary resuscitation (CPR). Surprisingly high numbers of patients haven't been asked if they want CPR, and many people would refuse it if asked. In a landmark study, Bedell and Delbanco reported that only 19 percent of the 154 patients who had been resuscitated in their hospital in 1981 had been asked earlier if they wanted to have CPR if it became necessary.[9] Eighty-six percent of the patients in their study were competent, and nearly all the physicians involved said they favored participation of patients in these decisions "at least sometimes." In almost a fifth of the cases, the families were consulted instead of the patients, although these patients were just as likely to be competent.

If their physicians had talked to these patients they would have been surprised. Of the twenty-four competent patients who survived to discharge, eight stated they had not desired CPR and wouldn't want it again, but only one of the sixteen physicians caring for these eight patients suspected the patient felt this way. In an accompanying editorial in the *New England Journal of Medicine*, Marcia Angell, M.D. suggests physicians ask their fully competent patient the following three questions:[10]

1. Do you wish to be fully informed of medical findings and consulted on all major decisions?
2. If so, do you have any objections to having your family informed as well as yourself?
3. If you do not wish to be fully informed, would you like to designate a family member or someone else to be informed in your stead?

By and large, Angell says, sick people have much the same

interest as healthy people in participating in decisions which affect them, and most patients probably want their families informed as well. However, nothing should be taken for granted. "What does the patient want? Ask him," she concludes.

The Doctor-Patient Relationship

Despite the problems both doctor and patient may have with the marriage of the concepts "informed" and "consent," informed consent is still the ideal because it can help doctors and patients talk with each other. Physicians need to see beyond the patients' "rights" to informed consent, and beyond physicians' "duty" to inform their patients to what is essentially a Christian imperative: Honor thy patient. Honor thy patient by talking to him or her as a person, as Jesus talked to people he encountered. Ethically valid consent is a process of shared decision making based on mutual respect and participation, an approach which characterizes the Christian's attitudes toward relationships. Jesus put it this way in Matthew 22:39–40: "You shall love your neighbor as yourself. On these two commandments [loving the Lord with your whole heart, soul, and mind, and loving your neighbor as yourself] depend the whole Law and the Prophets (NASB)."

The concept of informed consent at its deepest level—mutual love and respect—is in line with Jesus' teachings. While Jesus referred to religious law here, there is a sense in which the meaning of the civil law of informed consent also depends on these commandments, for otherwise it is a "useless ritual involving the recital of the contents of a form," in the words of the president's commission. Furthermore, in the actual clinical situations where the legal doctrine of informed consent is most difficult to enforce—those that involve the incompetent adult, the retarded child, the newborn, the unborn—it is precisely this mutual respect and honor for the other which enables physicians to care for patients in a manner which "fulfills the law."

I will address these clinical situations later in this chapter. For now let us turn to the common, "easy" situation of a doctor's relationship with a competent patient. This doctor-patient accommodation has been described by Dr. Mark Siegler:

> The nature of the patient involved—his personality, character, attitudes, and values—and the factors which led him to seek a medical encounter with this particular physician—are central components to the process. Similarly, the personality, character, attitude, values, and technical skills of the physician affect the accommodation. Further, the quality of the interaction between patient and physician—the chemistry of the interaction—modifies the process. Of course, the nature of the medical problem, including its type, acuteness, gravity, and its potential for remediation, will be a major determinant of whether a physician-patient accommodation is achieved. For example, the entire process will be modified profoundly and telescoped if the patient is acutely or critically ill and alternative medical resources are unavailable. Finally, other considerations which may affect the achievement of a physician-patient accommodation include clinical setting, e.g., a hospital, doctor's office, or the patient's home; the organization of the medical service; HMO or fee-for-service; and also, occasionally, the claims of other relevant third-party interests such as those of family, insurers, or the state.[11]

In each medical encounter, at each point, the patient and physician can arrive at a joint decision in which the physician agrees to care for the patient and the patient agrees to be treated by the physician. A physician is not obligated to enter a physician-patient relationship if he believes that he is unable to help the patient, or if he believes that even if he could help the patient he could do so only by sacrificing his own standards of what it means to be a good and responsible physician—in other words, if the relationship would result in an action the physician considers illegal or immoral.

In some situations, the physician will be largely in control, as in this case: A twenty-nine-year-old man is severely injured in an automobile accident. He is admitted to the emergency room, and it is apparent he is critically ill. There is no other emergency room in the area. The physician on call begins caring for him immediately.

In other situations, such as the following, the patient will be largely in control: A fifty-three-year-old man with well-controlled hypertension is experiencing impotence from his antihypertensive medication. His physician explains the risks of changing medications. The patient understands that another medication may not be as effective as the current one, but the patient strongly requests the change. His physician agrees to try another drug.

The particular balance of responsibilities may change with time and circumstances. It is not an easy relationship, not even when both physician and patient are open and sensitive. Physicians and other health professionals can share decision-making power with many of their patients, but there is a problem: how can physicians share decision-making power with noncompliant or incapacitated patients?

Noncompliance and the Case of Mrs. Sarah T.

Sarah T. was a forty-five-year-old white woman who had uncontrolled diabetes mellitus. She first came to see me in 1981 with severe retinopathy and a dorsal foot ulcer six by eight centimeters around and four centimeters in depth. The tendons of her foot were visible in the wound, and an x ray showed underlying osteomyelitis. Extensive skin grafting covered the wound, but the bone stayed infected despite long-term antibiotics. She required frequent hospitalization for foot ulcers. In the hospital on a diet, her blood sugars

were normal or low. Once home, her blood sugars rose again
to the 400 range and her insulin dosage had to be increased
again. Dozens of clinic visits followed over the next four
years. Her eye disease worsened; she had new foot ulcers.
When I made a house call, I found an eight-pack of Pepsi
and a bag of Snickers bars (the big ones) in her refrigerator.
I again discussed diet and adjusted her insulin dose upward.
One night the emergency room called: Sarah T. had gas gan-
grene. The surgeons amputated both legs above the knees.
She survived and was confined to a wheelchair.

One day she phoned me complaining of neck tightness. I
notified the paramedics, and in the emergency room her elec-
trocardiogram showed a large anterior wall myocardial infarction. She was admitted to the coronary care unit in congestive heart failure. The cardiologist said she needed a
Swan-Ganz catheter to monitor her cardiac pressures. I
talked with Sarah T. She was frightened. I assumed she was
worried about her recent heart attack and her difficulty with
breathing, but she told me her real fear: needles. She was
desperately afraid of needles and did not want the Swan because of the large needle.

Sarah T. and I often had difficulty arriving at a satisfactory physician-patient relationship, because she was afraid
I would stop caring for her if she told me the truth. She felt
guilty about her diet; I felt guilty that I couldn't help her
more and that her diabetes was hurting her so much. I can
honestly say I would not have abandoned her, because although I was not achieving my medical "goals," I felt I was
still able to help her through the various acute illnesses she
encountered.

Physicians often suspect (as I did with Sarah T.) that their
patients are noncompliant, and it should come as no surprise to caregivers that imperfection in diets, exercise, or
medication are common. According to an extensive review,
up to 50 percent of patients with hypertension fail to fol-

low referral advice; over 50 percent drop out of care in one year; and only about two-thirds of those who remain under care consume enough medication to adequately control their blood pressure. Noncompliance for short-term regimens is as high as 92 percent in careful studies. The problem cuts across all socioeconomic and educational boundaries; 50 percent of all patients for whom some appropriate therapy is prescribed fail to receive full benefit through inadequate adherence to treatment. Health professionals are notoriously noncompliant patients. Doctors, nurses, and allied health professionals often fail to take medicine properly.

Every clinician knows there are no pat answers for reaching a satisfactory doctor-patient relationship with noncompliant patients. These are some of our most "difficult" patients, because we cannot reach a true agreement easily. Working with such patients requires the qualities of mercy and patience. Physicians are imperfect imitators of God, who bears with us (and doesn't abandon us) through all our failures.

The Physician-Patient Relationship When the Patient Is Incapacitated

There are several groups of incapacitated patients. First are those "informed incapacitated" patients who may be elderly with mild dementia who are able to understand at one time but not another and whose capacity may vary from morning to night. Second are those who have been previously capacitated but are now incapacitated. Third are those who will never have decision-making capacity, such as the profoundly mentally retarded. Finally, there are those who lack capacity but have the potential to have decision-making capacity, like minor children or the unborn.

When physicians care for incapacitated patients, they assume more of the decision-making power. Advanced directives, in the form of living wills or durable powers of attorney, represent the wishes of once-decisional patients, so such directives enable patients to share some of the decision-making power even when they become incapacitated.[12] The following case illustrates the use of an advanced directive: A sixty-two-year-old man is admitted to the hospital after suffering a cardiac arrest. The patient is in a coma as a result of prolonged anoxia during the resuscitation. The patient has a living will, which states, "If I have an incurable injury I direct that life-sustaining procedures be withheld or withdrawn and that I be permitted to die naturally."

The patient's condition worsens and he develops acute renal failure. His physicians discuss dialysis with his wife. On the basis of knowing him and his stated wishes, she thinks he would refuse dialysis in his present condition. She asks his physicians not to dialyze him, and they agree.

Although a direct doctor-patient agreement with an incapacitated patient, like this patient in anoxic coma, is often impossible to achieve, a legitimate understanding can often be reached between the doctor and those who speak for the patient. While a decisional patient may refuse any treatment, the ability of the incapacitated person's "spokesperson" to refuse lifesaving treatment is properly somewhat more limited. As in this case, it must be based on what the patient would prefer *were he able to converse.*

Conclusion

As clinicians in the 1990s, many of us realize that we no longer want to live in a silent world; we wish to communicate and share our difficult decisions. Like patients, we are dissatisfied with a medical ethic that promulgates health-professional estrangement and patient isolation. The health-professional-patient relationship, a model of shared information and mutual consent, is a model which enables us to treat patients as human beings. This relationship also allows us to free the patient to accept (or reject) our advice.

There are problems with obtaining informed consent, respecting free will, and forging a health-professional-patient accommodation; these acts are intellectually challenging, emotionally trying, and time consuming for all involved. It was easier the old way. But my grandfather would be pleased that we are beginning to try to honor our patients as ourselves.

4

Shared Prayer

Our deepest beliefs and fears surface during moments of illness. We are embarrassed when we are forced to reveal how much we really care about ourselves and our loved ones and how frightened we really are. When health-caregivers look on the private terrors of their patients, they are often moved and humbled. A patient's dread of sickness and death is somehow both shameful and endearing.

How should caregiver and patient communicate at this critical juncture? This question is one of the most basic and important in medical practice. I would like to point out several approaches by drawing on observations I have made both on the mission field and in United States hospitals. I will use the situation of a clinical crisis during labor and delivery—surely one of the most anxiety-provoking situations in medicine.

Consider the following cases:

Case 1

The patient is a twenty-year-old Wisconsin woman who has been in labor for many hours without significant progress.

The obstetrician makes a diagnosis of "failure to progress" and informs the patient that a Cesarean section is indicated. She explains the risks of C-section—bleeding, infection, and rarely, mortality—but recommends the procedure because of its safety for both the woman and her baby when compared with the alternative. The most worrisome risks to the child of continued labor, she says, are brain damage or even death. The patient expresses concern over the baby's status and consents to a C-section.

The anesthesiologist then explains the spinal anesthetic procedure, telling the patient that its risks are low but that occasionally a patient's blood pressure may drop; sometimes scarring can occur in the area surrounding the injection in the spinal canal; some patients will experience spinal headaches. The patient nods assent, signs the form, and tells the anesthesiologist to go ahead. He asks her to let him know if she has any questions as he is doing the procedure. The anesthesia and C-section proceed without incident. A healthy infant is delivered.

Case 2

The patient is a twenty-year-old West African woman who is also not progressing in labor, and the missionary physician informs the patient that she should probably have a C-section for her own sake and for that of the baby. She nods an initial assent. He then asks her if she would like to pray about the surgery with him and with the other doctors and nurses. He begins the prayer by asking God to help the patient and her child during the C-section. He asks that God guide his hands and those of the anesthesiologist as they do their work and that the woman and her child will be kept safe from the dangers of the surgery. The woman says a similar prayer, asking that the doctors' work will go well, that the child will be protected from harm and be born alive in the world. The anesthesia and C-section proceed without incident. A healthy infant is delivered.

Both of these C-sections were performed by technically competent physicians and were identical in many ways. The same anesthetic agent was administered and the same surgical technique was employed; even the ligatures were similar. Both patients were black and poor; both physicians were devoutly religious and regarded their practices as mission work; both surgeries took place in hospitals with a religious affiliation. In both cases the outcome was favorable.

In America, the patient gave informed consent to the procedure; in Africa, the patient and the physician prayed together about it. The differences between these preoperative approaches to informing and comforting are revealing, both culturally and spiritually. Let's examine this distinction between first-world ethics and two-thirds-world faith.

Distinction between Ethics and Faith

The first case I presented—the woman with a C-section who gave consent for both the C-section and the spinal anesthesia—involved such a process. The patient took part in the decision-making process; she was treated as a person with a voice to be heard. She might have refused the particular form of anesthesia she was offered; she might even have opted to refuse the C-section, although in clinical practice such refusals are extremely rare. I think the most positive aspects of informed consent can be illustrated by cases like hers; there is evidence of mutual respect between doctor and patient at a point in which the patient needs an advocate.

But what of the second case? What analogous part does shared prayer play in preoperative counseling for a C-section in a two-thirds-world setting?

"Prayer is to religion," P. T. Forsythe noted, "what original research is to science." Thomas Merton pointed out that through prayer we demonstrate a yearning for the simple presence of God, for a personal understanding of his word, for knowledge of his will, and for the ability to hear and obey him.[1] A.W. Tozer put it this way: "To have found God and still pursue Him is the soul's paradox of love, scorned indeed by the too easily satisfied religionist, but justified in happy experience by the children of the burning heart."[2] While prayer is directed to God by those who seek him, it also enables us to better know ourselves. Augustine exclaimed, *"Noverim te, noverim me"* ("May I know you, may I know myself"). Despite this consensus on the importance of prayer, it seems that prayer is relatively infrequent in the clinical setting in the United States. Most Christian physicians I know (including myself) do not pray with most of their patients. Even in institutions with religious affiliation, prayer is often relegated to the loudspeakers and printed cards or delegated to the appropriate specialists—clergy! An analysis of the reasons for this attitude toward prayer would probably turn on the increasing pluralism within our society and a growing sense on the part of many that religion is at best irrelevant and at worst a dangerous impediment. The medical centers in which prayer and medicine are linked are viewed with distrust by many of our citizens, as if prayer somehow diminishes the power of modern medicine. One wonders what would happen to the "image" of many prominent hospitals and clinics if their doctors began routinely praying with patients.

Thus, in the first world, at critical times in patients' lives and at crucial decision-making points, information-related activities like obtaining informed consent often predominate over spiritual activities. Mind predominates over soul. While these information-related activities are very important and necessary, so is prayer. But prayer differs from providing information in both its object and its expectation.

The object of prayer is God; one prays to God to receive answers, to confess, to intercede for others, to plead, to give thanks. The doctor and patient in the second case asked God for a safe surgery, pleading, in a sense, for safe passage through what they both knew was a dangerous situation. Granted, the American patient knew better than the African patient just how dangerous the surgery was; informed consent is more effective than prayer at imparting specific risk information. But the African woman knew the C-section involved surgery, and even those without knowledge in statistics must know surgery is dangerous.

The doctor's prayer was also intercessory in nature, because he prayed on behalf of the patient. While both doctor and patient heard each other, their preoperative prayer was to God; this differs from preoperative informed consent, the object of which is the patient. In the prayer the patient puts herself finally in God's hands; in the case of informed consent she learns what risk she takes in putting herself in the doctor's hands. Of course, informed consent and prayer are not mutually exclusive, but there are fundamental differences behind the object of informed consent and prayer, the one human-based—mental—the other God based—spiritual.

The expectations of informed consent and prayer follow from their objects. The purpose of providing information is to enable patient participation, and the expectation is that the doctor will honor the principles of fidelity, veracity, and competency. Mistakes will happen. Outcomes may be adverse. But the patient agrees to the possibility of these mistakes and shares the burden of decisions which lead to maloccurrences. The expectation of prayer is that God will answer, although in many cases God's answer may be no, may be withheld, delayed, exceed the petition, or be different from the request.

While those who pray know the possibility of other answers, they expect that God will act beneficently in the end. Like Paul, they might cite the goodness of God or the great-

ness of his love for us: "For I am convinced that neither
death nor life, nor angels nor demons, neither the present
nor the future, nor any powers, neither height nor depth,
nor anything else in all creation will be able to separate us
from the love of God, that is in Christ Jesus our Lord" (Rom.
8:38–39). While the African patient may expect the missionary physician to be truthful and competent as well, the
main expectation fostered by prayer is that God will guide
the surgeon and watch over the surgery. Bad things may still
happen, but only as allowed by God.

Despite their striking differences in object and expectation, the clinical ability of both informed consent and prayer
to involve patients and reassure them is quite similar. The
American patient feels she has been consulted; she has been
treated as a person; she knows her physician cares enough
about her to attend her respectfully. The African patient
also feels she has been involved; the doctor prays with her
as a fellow seeker, as a fellow human being. He cares about
her enough to ask for the best help he thinks he can get—
that which only God can give him. Both patients are put at
ease. Their C-sections are performed by surgeons who have
made culturally validated attempts—through first-world
ethics in one case and two-thirds-world faith in the other—
to show how much they care. In both cases, there is effective communication.

Conclusion

Medical ethics need not be separate from faith, whether
we live in the first world or the two-thirds world. Both mind
and soul are involved in bodily healing. Many patients would
feel comforted in either setting by the offer of both information and spiritual communication with God. The psalmist
knew the need of this comfort: "Give ear to my words, O
LORD, consider my sighing. Listen to my cry for help, my
King and my God; for to you I pray. In the morning, O LORD,

you hear my voice; in the morning I lay my requests before you and wait in expectation" (Ps. 5:1–3). When faced with personal terror in our moments of illness, we could benefit from prayer.

We have a choice in the way we live our faith before God and each other. We are part of a pluralistic culture, but we can be more than sightseers. Perhaps E.W. Oldenburg puts it best in his poem "In Canterbury Cathedral":

> On a day sweet with April showers the safe tires of our
>   tour bus had sung us south from London.
> Sightseer pilgrims, cameras slung, no need or time on pa-
>   tient plodding horses for long diverting tales.
> We stood at last at Beckett's shrine, lost in architecture
>   and dates, confused by Norman and Gothic.
> Our ancient tiny guide seemed shrunk into his suit,
>   dwarfed by his clothes as we all were dwarfed by time.
> His small precise English voice went on:
> pronounced "Our Lord," and the words fell on us like a
>   benediction.
> "Our"—incredible assumption of union offered in passing
>   to American strangers,
> mortar for diverse motley stones.
> Time and blood and history redeemed from meaningless-
>   ness: two words turned sightseers into pilgrims.

Part Two

Comforting the Sick

5

Colleagues in Ministry

The Pastor and the Health Professional

Allie is a third-year medical student, and she is making rounds today not with me but with the hospital chaplain. She is learning the ministry skills that the chaplain can teach her: listening, reading Scripture, and praying at the patient's bedside, if the patient is amenable. She learns about the unique role the chaplain plays in the hospital, from comforting families in the emergency room to discussing a patient's surgery on the first postoperative day.

Our local chapter of the Christian Medical & Dental Society has worked closely with the chaplains in setting up this special program. The students are fortunate, because they are learning one of the most important practices any Christian health professional can learn: a close working relationship with a key professional colleague, a clergyperson.

As they visit my patient, who has severe alcoholism and is jaundiced due to liver disease, I note that Allie and the

chaplain discuss the patient's spiritual concerns as well as
the medical findings. It is wonderful to see a medical student round with a chaplain. Many practicing physicians
seem not even to recognize their hospital's chaplaincy service, but Allie and some of her fellow students are already
learning to be colleagues in ministry with the chaplains.

Chaplains are especially useful members of ethics committees, and I have found several cases in which the chaplain's input solved the case. For example, the family of one
young man who had suffered severe brain injury was having trouble deciding whether or not to consent to tube feeding and continued antibiotic therapy and several needed surgical procedures. Many of these procedures were necessary
for his comfort, but the family members, particularly the father, had almost irrationally refused them all. Some am-
bivalence was understandable, but the patient was not brain
dead and might possibly be able to recover some function
with continued support.

The ethics committee met, and despite my best ethical and
clinical arguments, the father and mother were obviously
angry. They looked away during my discussion. Then the
hospital clergy member spoke up. "Has your faith been a
factor in all of this?" he asked. The patient's father said yes.
"Well, you need to put him in God's hands, then," the chaplain said. The father visibly relaxed, and the mother began
to cry. They then talked about their son, story after story.
In the end they consented to some of the treatments and
were planning to consider the others.

I was, frankly, stunned. The chaplain's statement seemed
almost a platitude, and yet the family had reacted so posi-
tively. But later, as I discussed the case with the chaplain, I
found that he had been visiting the patient daily and helping
the family work through their anger at God. Somehow, as
they had decided to relinquish control of their son's case to
God, they found a measure of peace and, as they told the sto-

ries, began to think about his medical care in a more rational way. All the clinical and ethical arguments that I and other committee members had made didn't break through. The chaplain's simple but perceptive spiritual approach turned the entire situation around. I value the clergy members of my ethics committees and enjoy teaching chaplains in training programs about being on ethics committees. Ethics consultation is a practical and helpful way for hospital chaplains to have valuable clinical input as colleagues.

Another very useful collegial situation is when the chaplain or pastor consults with the physician. The pastor initiates the consultation. For example, a pastor called me to see Mr. Carlsen, a patient from his church dying of lung cancer in a nearby hospital who wanted to make a durable power of attorney. I went to his bedside. Mr. Carlsen was in a very receptive mood, and after we talked about his upcoming death, I asked him if he wished to pray. He nodded assent. As we prayed, his eyes filled with tears. It is not unusual for patients who are completing an advance directive to be very open spiritually, and on several occasions I have found this to be a good time to work with a pastor. I have also prayed along with the pastors from my own church for various church members who have requested it. I am often deeply touched by this form of co-ministry and always hope that it does as much for the patient as it does for me.

Pastors have called me to see patients they are counseling to evaluate them for underlying medical illness. I consider this a valuable consultation. I try to evaluate the patient medically and report back to the pastor, if the patient consents to this report, just as I would report back to a physician colleague who refers me to a patient.

The partnership, then, can work both ways. Students and physicians-in-training can learn ministry skills by making rounds with chaplains or local pastors. Clergypersons who wish to be on ethics committees can learn some clinical

skills from doing consultations. They can also refer patients
they are counseling to a physician colleague for medical
evaluation.

As we work together in the hospital, however, I find that
most doctors and many clergypersons are uncomfortable
crossing sectarian lines. In one hospital I worked at several
years ago, we had a Protestant chaplain, a Catholic chaplain, and a rabbi. Each was excellent in serving patients
within his own faith tradition. I would see one of them as I
walked through the hospital to see my patients and would
ask one, how "so-and-so" was doing. Often the reply was,
"Oh, he's Catholic. He's not one of mine." Initially I found
this troubling, but then after a while I realized that, just as
I would not presume to see a patient who "belonged" to another doctor, these chaplains would not see patients who
"belonged" to another faith tradition. But interestingly,
many of my patients did not want to be labeled as Lutheran,
Catholic, or Jewish. They might have New Age or some idio-
syncratic belief system, yet I felt they could benefit from seeing a member of the clergy. So I found another chaplain who
was willing to be flexible, work with the unlabeled patients,
and deal with those who didn't fit anyone's list. Given this
panel of chaplains, I was able to consult with the chaplaincy
service on most cases, unless the patients refused.

I find a kindly attitude, a willingness to listen and pray,
and an openness to reading the Scriptures to be the most clinically relevant characteristics of chaplains I like to consult
regarding my patients. I very much like our chaplain who is
a Catholic priest and particularly appreciate his clinical touch.
Chaplains may not be exactly in the patient's or physician's
denominational tradition, but they still can do a wonderful
job with and for the patient. This can be a big stretch when
the Christian doctor is dealing with patients who do not belong to a Christian faith tradition. But the stretch is necessary and often worthwhile. For instance, I have learned a lot

from working with a rabbi who taught a course at the medical school on Jewish medical ethics. I consider all of the chaplains at our hospital to be colleagues, and while I do not agree with the theology of some of them, I must remember they have a First Amendment right to minister to patients of their own faith tradition at our public hospital. And I find that when my patients have been ministered to in a spiritual sense they feel better, get better faster, are less afraid of treatment, and are, in many cases, less afraid of suffering and death.

The reality of the modern hospital, even the modern religious hospital, is that Lutheran hospitals have Muslim patients, Catholic hospitals Jehovah's Witness patients, Jewish hospitals Methodist patients. All health professionals and chaplains need to be flexible. We use our medical skills to treat every patient who comes to us. We use our listening skills and comforting and prayerful touch as clergy to help every patient who is willing, even though many will not see things our way or say prayers our way.

Still, despite varied religious backgrounds of chaplains, many give very similar counsel to patients. For example, on an ethics committee chaplains of different faith traditions frequently agree on a proper course of treatment. They have in common rigorous ways of approaching clinical situations, tend to be highly educated individuals, and thus may analyze situations in ways similar to other professionals. Often there is very little disagreement between the chaplain, the physician, the hospital administrator, and the ethics committee attorney. I hope this is because we are looking at the same facts in the same case. I always insist that when we do an ethics consultation, we each personally see the patient so that we can see eye-to-eye and talk about the same patient. We all care about the patient, and the areas of common ground help bring consensus in most cases.

The strong ethical framework of many church pastors and hospital chaplains is particularly significant to the work.

Many pastors know what they think about cases because they are well studied in their own value systems. When I present cases to them, they can be of practical help and can explain why they would make one decision over another. Many people lack this sort of ethical framework and have to consider each case as if it were handed down *de novo*. But a pastor who is a colleague in ministry has the framework, and probably a number of past cases, to draw on.

Pastors and health professionals are colleagues who can help patients work through issues of suffering. Many patients have legitimate concerns about physical suffering even before it occurs. How and when will I die? Will it be with dehydration, or with infection, or perhaps a pneumonia? Will my pain be treated aggressively, or will I be abandoned in my suffering? Will I be alone, short of breath, and frightened, or will I be cared for and comforted? Modern physicians need extra help in this area. Like our patients, we find it difficult to accept suffering as part of this "vale of tears." Suffering is considered optional. Is the suffering worth it? Is the pain worth the gain? Since there sometimes seems to be little to gain in the treatment of painful or terminal illness, a patient may choose to end his or her suffering. But which method? On what is the decision based? Must a decision be made? When? By whom? These questions, which are medical, philosophical, religious, and enormously personal, especially the question of suffering, can often best be answered in a particular patient's case by the physician working with a clinically sensitive pastor or chaplain. These issues transcend the ordinary clinical understanding of a patient's case. The chaplain can be the interpreter of suffering, can help move the problem beyond a simple pain/gain calculus.

When I consider this medical-clerical relationship and how complex and vital it can be, I am reminded of a patient of mine named Mary.

She was a big woman sitting in the chair next to my desk, watching me warily as I closed the door. In her hands she held a carpetbag; her legs guarded a plastic shopping sack from an elegant women's clothing store. The sack was overflowing with various articles of dirty laundry. She had a musty smell about her; the room reminded me of the 27th Street exit by the Red Star yeast factory on a cold winter day, a faint but distinct, instantly recognizable smell.

I knew what her feet would smell like: down around 6th Street in the stockyards on a hot summer day, the animal stink lightened a bit by the sweeter smell of sweat we humans have on our feet and often in our armpits, depending on the resident bacteria.

I sniffed subconsciously several times while saying hello and surmised that Mary hadn't bathed in weeks, was probably homeless, might have a skin infection with yeast. I couldn't smell cigarettes on her clothing or breath and she didn't smell like any particular brand of booze. (Physicians often write incorrectly, "Patient smells of alcohol." Actually, alcohol has no smell. It is the other components of alcoholic beverages which smell, often uniquely: the sour smell of whiskey breath, the cutting odor of wine breath, the bitter smell of beer breath.)

Like many homeless persons, Mary wore a coat too warm for the weather—certainly too warm for the stuffy examination room. But you get cold if you stay out all night; the chill comes slowly at dusk and lasts interminably throughout the night. In Wisconsin it would be reasonable to wear a stiff coat most nights of the year if you sleep unsheltered. Hers was almost fashionable, a kind of dark worsted wool with little white and brown nibs. Her skin showed some signs of aging; she had many of the little brown heaped-up lesions called seborrheic keratoses. The whites of her eyes were slightly yellowed. She did not paint her fingernails. She wore a thick, blue-stoned ring on her left fourth finger whose symbolism and value were difficult to appraise.

Her boots were partly unlaced and tied in the kind of knot at the back which you tie if you walk a lot and are tired of having a bow come undone all the time. She wore the high gray wool socks with red-striped tops that army surplus stores sell. Her main problem, she said, was her feet. They swell. They hurt when she is up walking all day, and they get a little better at night when she rests. Another doctor gave her water pills, which helped the swelling. Would I give her pills too?

Yes, she says, she does live on the streets until it gets real cold. She has one sister who knows about her but lives in another city.

She fumbles in her carpetbag and finds that an old, crusty-topped bottle of Vaseline Intensive Care lotion has somehow spilled inside. She carefully wipes the tan goop from a small case in the bag and explores under it to see what else might have been affected by the spill.

The examination revealed what I expected, except her feet smelled worse than I thought they would because of the wool socks. Her lower legs had 1–2+ pitting edema. Her blood pressure was high, but she was not in heart failure. She had signs of longstanding venous disease in her legs; she needed to stop standing around all the time, keep her feet up more, and wear tight leg hose like Jobst stockings. I needed to check some blood and make sure her kidneys, liver, potassium, and protein were normal, and that she was not anemic. I would try a water pill to treat her blood pressure; it would help the swelling a little too, but not completely since her problem was more one of gravity than of fluid overload. She also needed mammograms, stool screening for blood, a flu shot, maybe a chest x ray and EKG.

"I don't want none of that, doctor. But I will take the water pills. They help me."

"But we have to do the tests to make sure there's nothing . . . "

"Doctor, thank-you, but I have to go before it gets dark. I can't be getting tests." She stirs, wary again, ready to leave. She gets up.

"Will you come and see us again?" I ask.

"Oh, yes, doctor. I always come here to the County when I need help. Could I have the pills for my feet?"

She is gone quickly, leaving me alone in the room with the vague smell of her all around, a smell I can no longer place.

The story could end here, and usually it does. I gave Mary a few water pills, and she seemed satisfied. But I noticed that Mary was staying, at least for the time being, at the rescue mission. I knew the pastor there, having worked as a volunteer in their Tuesday evening clinic.

Mary was not as alone as she seemed. One of my colleagues was also seeing her. Maybe together we could make a difference.

6

High Technology Medicine

Comforting a Modern Job in the ICU

Job continued his discourse:
"Terrors overwhelm me;
my dignity is driven away as by the wind,
my safety vanishes like a cloud.
And now my life ebbs away;
days of suffering grip me.
Night pierces my bones;
my gnawing pains never rest.
My skin grows black and peels;
My body burns with fever."
—Job 29:1; 30:15–17, 30

Hospitals are places of pain and suffering, and intensive care units distill human agony. They are the places where we would find a modern Job—a patient with a life-threatening disease who is febrile and possibly septic. In the modern ICU patients are frightened and overwhelmed by the severity of their illnesses and the inescapable presence of high technology. Their "dignity is driven away as by the wind": hospital workers regulate patients' bowels and bladders and examine, feed, wash, and turn them. But it is also in the ICU that they, like Job, might survive a near fatal illness.

Critical illness is often accompanied by loneliness and disorientation. Job describes the feeling: "My safety vanishes like a cloud." Unfortunately, studies reveal we need to improve our comforting opportunities. A survey of visiting policies in seventy-eight ICUs in Ohio demonstrated that 25 percent allowed only two visits per day, and 42 percent restricted visits to under twenty minutes. Most units rarely or never allowed children under twelve to visit. The authors of the study point out that there is no empiric medical evidence which supports the need for these sorts of policies.[1] Field studies of physician behavior in the ICU reveal a focus on laboratory evaluation rather than on patients, a lack of expression of personal feelings, and an excessive dependence on invasive technology. One of these studies records an example of the focus on the status of the machinery instead of the care of the patient:

"A preadolescent boy, hospitalized with leukemia, became severely immunocompromised by his therapy. He developed pneumocystic carinii pneumonia and his condition rapidly deteriorated. He required ventilatory assistance . . . arterial cutdowns and a Swan-Ganz catheter. Numerous complications developed. One morning after a long and complicated presentation of serial blood gas determinations, pulmonary wedge pressures, intake and output, and similar material, a staff anesthesiologist commented that everything 'seemed alright.' The weary resident who had made the presentation replied uncomfortably, 'Yeah, except the kid.'"[2]

We are providing technology in the ICU. Now we need to learn to provide comfort. In this chapter I will examine the nature of intensive care and suggest some solutions for better comforting "Job" in the ICU. These solutions must consider the positive aspects as well as the limits of the technological imperative. Let's begin by examining the development of ICU technology.

Development of ICU Technology

Thirty-five years ago a patient with failure of the heart, lungs, kidneys, or gastrointestinal tract died within a few minutes, days, or weeks. G. D. Phillips traces the development of life-support systems as shown in the following table.[3]

Historical Development of ICU Technology

Cardiopulmonary Resuscitation (CPR)

1847 Internal heart massage in cats
1901 Successful internal cardiac massage in a woman who collapsed during chloroform anesthesia
1947 Internal cardiac defibrillation
1956 External cardiac defibrillation
1958 Mouth-to-mouth resuscitation

Artificial Ventilation

1776 Bellows for resuscitating the drowned
1932 Artificial ventilation in anesthesia
1940 First ventilator
1953 Use of ventilator in polio patient

Dialysis

1923 First peritoneal dialysis in man
1947 First hemodialysis

Intravenous Feeding

1800 Intravenous dextrose

1920 Intravenous fats
1937 Intravenous amino acids
1968 Complete intravenous feeding

Intensive Care Units

1958 Baltimore City Hospital ICU
Toronto General Hospital ICU
1988 Over 5000 ICU's worldwide

Most technologies, such as CPR and artificial ventilation, were limited to animal experimentation until the 1920s and 1930s, and much of the actual development occurred after 1950.

For example, external cardiac defibrillation began in 1956, and the use of mouth-to-mouth resuscitation became widespread in the late 1950s and early 1960s. There may, however, be much older examples of resuscitation. Elisha put his full weight on the body of a dead child and put his mouth on the child's mouth, then repeated the maneuver; the child returned to life (2 Kings 4:32–35). Fourteenth-century patients who suffered cardiac arrest were whipped with nettles, and in the seventeenth century they were draped over a trotting horse, without reported success. Choosing among these three techniques would be easy. I personally would have wished to forego resuscitation (be DNR) in the fourteenth and seventeenth centuries. Those readers who are sometimes concerned about the violent aspects of modern CPR may find its historical precedents interesting.

Thus, we may draw the following three conclusions from our review of the development of ICU technology:

1. ICU technology as we know it has developed within our lifetimes.

2. There are mechanical emergency support or resuscitation systems for most of the vital organ systems except the brain and the liver.
3. Since 1958 intensive care has grown into a multidisciplinary and multinational endeavor.

The Critique of High Technology

Despite the clear benefits of ICU technology—improved survival for patients with trauma and some critical illnesses—there has been some criticism of medical technology. Several studies have shown that some patients with acute myocardial infarction or acute pulmonary edema may survive just as well outside of the ICU as in it. Data collected on the neonatal ICU confirm that gains have been made in the survival of infants with increasingly lower birth weights: in the 1960s the limit for giving ventilatory support was 1500 grams; in 1970 it was 1000 grams; in 1975 it was 750 grams; and now the limit is around 500 grams. The success, however, is not unqualified. Ventilatory management has been difficult, and multiple medical complications may occur. The tiny infant may have patent ductus arteriosus, immature brain and germinal matrix, and incomplete vascularization of the retina. Increased attention and funding of neonatal intensive-care technology may be diverting attention and funding from basic prenatal care and primary care pediatrics.

Some outspoken critics of modern medicine, like Ivan Illich, question whether many significant gains have been made in the recent technological revolution. I must admit that as a physician I am taken aback by this kind of antitechnological sentiment. Like most clinicians, I am generally favorable to technological advances because I see many of them help my patients on a day-to-day basis. Technology is a double-edged sword, but it often allows us to reverse physiological processes which threaten our patients' lives.

We know adequate food and housing, proper sanitation, and childhood immunizations are more potent lifesavers than are arterial lines. But arterial lines work very well if the patient is hypotensive and hypoxic. Why, then, the critique of high technology?

The Problem of the Technological Imperative

Perhaps we can find the answer in one of the most eloquent of the antitechnology voices, Christian philosopher Jacques Ellul. In his work *The Technological Society*,[4] Ellul makes the following points:

1. Ours is a progressively technical civilization.
2. The ever-expanding and irreversible rule of technology is extended to all domains of life.
3. Our civilization is committed to the quest for continually improved means to carelessly examined ends.
4. What was once prized in its own right now becomes worthwhile only if it helps to achieve something else.
5. Technique turns means into ends.
6. "Know-how" takes on ultimate value.

The problem, according to Ellul, is that technology does this without plan; it just happens, as a sort of technological imperative. ICU technology is used because it is the ultimate medical "know-how." Continual improvement in machinery is sought while the medical ends of the technology are only hastily examined. Ellul's critique must be acknowledged as at least partly valid. Better technological assessment is needed. But caregivers, in general, are grateful for the benefits of technology.

The caring imperative in medicine preceded the technological imperative, and for all its science, medicine remains an art. Part of the art of modern medicine is the ability to use technology without being enamored with it to the detriment of the patient. "Know-how" is important but should not take on ultimate value in medical care; we prize the patient in his or her own right as a person. Let's return, then, to the care of "Job." How do we provide better comfort to him in our modern ICU's?

About 70 percent of patients and families who had previously experienced ICU care would be willing to undergo ICU care again to achieve even one month of survival; 8 percent were unwilling to undergo ICU care to achieve any prolongation of life. These data suggest that besides our perception of the enormous value of an identifiable life, patient preferences for ICU care are strong.[5]

This is the case even though the ICU is a frightening place, and too often we "comfort" the Jobs in our ICUs with the use of high technology alone. Technological comfort is expensive and it does not address the frightening loss of control, dignity, and purpose experienced by the seriously ill patient: "Terrors overwhelm me." The ICU can become a place where doctors strive to outdo each other, where hospitals compete against each other, where money is made, and where patients suffer, often alone. But the ICU should be a life-saving place. Is there a better way? Let's go back to what we learn from those who sought to comfort Job.

Compassionate ICU Care

ICU care can be more compassionate. Recall the story of Job.

1. Job needed human understanding and sensitive spiritual counsel. This would seem to be important in the modern ICU. Often nurses provide excellent comfort care; physicians need to learn from them how to be more compassionate to ICU patients. Often patients can remember their ICU nurses but only recall physicians "picking" at them "like white-coated gulls." Patients fear abandonment. Patients need a sense of control, a sense that their care-

givers respect and honor them. We need to pay attention to the patient rather than concentrate solely on the data. We need to be sensitive to patients' spiritual needs, and if we are not comfortable addressing them, we need to enlist the help of our spiritual colleagues, the clergy or the hospital chaplain.

2. While we should attempt to use appropriate technology, we need to recognize when technology is futile and may no longer serve us but, rather, threatens to master us. Professional ego, fear of litigation, competition, and remuneration are entwined with the use of high technology in too many circumstances. The critics of technology rightly argue against these reasons for its use. Medical science should serve the patient.

3. Despite legitimate criticism of high technology medicine, however, the ICU care of Job and patients like him reflects a high view of human beings as persons whose lives are worth saving despite the time and the cost. Furthermore, ICU care upholds a traditional medical value which is being increasingly attacked—that of prolonging or saving lives.

Conclusion

If I were Job's doctor and he consented to aggressive treatment, I would admit him to the ICU and let his friends and family visit him. I would ask the hospital chaplain to see him also (just in case his friends gave him bad advice). I would use appropriate technology to treat his infection, skin disease, and fever, and I would prescribe pain medication to control his "gnawing pains." I would encourage the nurses to sit with him, and I would try to do the same. If I thought Job were dying despite ICU care, I would speak with him and his family and work out a treatment plan which would emphasize support and comfort. I would assure him that I would not abandon him even if he chose supportive care rather than ICU care.

But on occasion I might hope for the best:

After this, Job lived a hundred and forty years; he saw his children and their children to the fourth generation. And so he died, old and full of years (Job 42:16).

7

Treating "Gomers"

Medical Case History

"Mr. Wyeth came in again last night," said an intern to his resident before rounds with their staff physician. "His bedsore is worse, and he has his usual bilateral aspiration pneumonia. His feeding tube came out at the nursing home, so I put it in again. Since he has the "O" sign, I ordered an x ray to be sure the tube is in his stomach instead of his lungs."

The resident laughed cynically. "What a gomer. Just watch him, and make sure he doesn't develop the dotted 'O' sign. We don't want to be scraping maggots out of his bedsore."

Medical Case Discussion

Mr. Wyeth is a patient who has been admitted "again." He has had frequent episodes of pneumonia due to aspiration—the inhalation of stomach contents. Despite a feeding tube to prevent him from swallowing food down into his lungs, he continues to aspirate. This implies he has a severe brain dysfunction causing the loss of his gag reflex. Alzheimer's disease has also affected his ability to think; he is unconscious.

The terms the intern used to describe the physical exam were popularized by the satirical book *The House of God*,[1] which was written about modern medical training by an intern in a "house of God" (teaching hospital). The author, Samuel Shem, M.D., refers to patients like Mr. Wyeth as "gomers," an acronym for Get Out of My Emergency Room. (Astute Bible students also recognize Gomer as a son of Japheth [Gen. 10:2], a people [Ezek. 38:6], and the wife of Hosea [Hos. 1:3]). One of many "rules" of *The House of God* is that gomers return again and again to the hospital with the same problem. According to Shem, the "O" sign describes a gomer's constantly open, moaning mouth. The "dotted O" refers to a fly landing on a gomer's exposed tongue.

As a beginning medical student I was shocked to hear such conversations. As an intern I laughed in bitterness and fatigue at such words. As a harried resident I grew to understand the satire. As a staff physician I continue to search for ways to make medical training more humane, to improve physicians' and other health-care workers' attitudes, and to foster compassion. As a Christian I find solace and modeling in Jesus' words and attitudes, which are as logical and compelling in the intensive care unit or hospital floor or nursing home unit as they were at the tomb of Lazarus.

Cynicism:
Denying the Wound, Withdrawing from Decay

Cynicism is the tendency to doubt the value of high ideals or to question the sincerity of those who express such ideals. It is the belief that all human action is the result of self-interest. The language and humor of *The House of God* reveal the disillusionment and cynicism felt by many young physicians and nurses. Why do these intelligent, idealistic, caring young people become cynical? Why do studies show that medical students become progressively more cynical while in training? For young physicians-in-training, cynicism is an easy way to get needed psychological distance from emotional situations in medical school and on the wards.

Cynicism is distancing, but I don't think the students' main need is to distance themselves from competition or anxiety. I also don't believe time is the problem—it takes only a moment to feel compassion. Judging from my own experience, I think the problem is even more basic. Physicians and nurses and other caregivers possess the human tendency to deny wounds and withdraw from decay. They are supposed to embrace the sick and offer compassionate hands to the dying while they practice their art. But their own flesh recoils at the thought of disease and contagion. They do not want to be fellow sufferers; they want to cure the wound so they don't have to look at it any longer.

Health-caregivers are immersed in disease. While in training I cared for critically ill patients with coronary disease, cancer, kidney failure, and emphysema. Sometimes I was awake for thirty-six hours straight monitoring vital signs, checking serum electrolytes, inserting intravenous catheters, ordering medications. I began to learn that the sick keep coming, day after day and year after year. I couldn't cure them all; they were dying despite my best efforts. I began withdrawing, distancing, walking in wider circles around the beds. I couldn't live up to my ideals of cure. The wounds were everywhere, and I wanted to avoid them. It was natural. Why did the priest and the Levite pass the wounded man who fell among robbers (the story of the good Samaritan, Luke 10:30–37)? Was part of the reason, at least, that they were afraid of seeing his wounds, becoming involved in them, binding them? Why did Martha recoil at the thought of removing the stone from Lazarus' tomb (John 11:39)? Wasn't she afraid of the stench of decay? Why are cancer and AIDS patients sometimes rejected by friends and family? It is quite easy to be cynical—to deny the wound or withdraw from decay. Physicians, nurses, and other health-care workers are more exposed to wounds and decay than the average person and develop a formalized defense and denial mechanism: cynicism, as exemplified by the language and values of *The House of God*. But meanwhile, underneath, we want to embrace the value of the person's life. Underneath we want to love the person. So we feel even more guilty. We are denying our calling, and then we are also being defensive about our denial. And we deny our own woundedness.

Compassion:
Binding the Wounds, Preparing for Burial

The good Samaritan, Jesus said, felt compassion, came to the wounded man, poured oil and wine on his wounds, and bandaged them. Then he brought him to an inn and took care of him. The good nurse puts a dressing on Mr. Wyeth's bedsore. The good physician tries to keep him comfortable and pain-free. Like the good Samaritan, the good caregiver does these things compassionately. He or she does not try to keep the wounded man alive forever, but also does not deny the need of the wounded person.

Other aspects of compassion that Jesus illustrates involve the discussion of death accompanied by spiritual counseling, pain control, and caring presence during and after death. Jesus freely discussed his death and the death of others throughout his ministry. When Mary took the costly perfume of pure nard and anointed his feet, he considered the act as burial preparation. Christian caregivers need to discuss illness and suffering with their patients, focusing honestly on the unpleasant, fearful aspects—the aspects which troubled even Jesus' soul (John 12:27). Physicians, nurses, and clergy can give spiritual counsel, testifying that in Jesus there is light and life.

Just as Jesus was offered the wine, so dying patients need to have pain control. Even the brutal executioners considered this aspect of Jesus' death. Caregivers must assiduously use effective pain-reducing regimens. For Jesus, the final acts of human compassion were performed by family and friends. Mary, Jesus' mother, Mary the wife of Cleophas, and Mary Magdalene stood at the foot of his cross. Joseph of Arimathea and Nicodemus wrapped his body with linens and spices, as was the burial custom; Mary Magdalene, Mary the mother of James, and Salome brought more spices to anoint him on Easter morning. These before-and-after-death examples of compassion serve as models for modern caregivers, who stand at the foot of the bed. We can be there with the dying and the family, and even attend the funeral.

Jesus teaches us a far more realistic approach, one which involves keeping company with the sufferer. His stories show caregivers staying with the sick, even though they acknowledge the difficulty. We are not called to be superhuman, just the opposite. We can give others comfort because we can receive comfort. We don't have to be cynical— our ideals were too high because they were self-imposed standards of perfection and obsession and guilt-avoidance. We don't have to fight death and wounds by ourselves. We can go up, we can look up; we are not alone, even when we are wounded ourselves. These are the rules of the real house of God.

8

Scar Watcher

I am an unabashed scar watcher. I have seen some beauties in my day: long, livid knife streaks across backs; abdomens with crossing, circling cicatrices; scars from burns, gunshots, crush injuries, open fractures.

Admittedly, it is not a glamorous occupation, but scar watching is actually quite popular. There are few glimpses as revealing as the sight of a scar. Each scar has a story, and as I look at a scar I wonder, and often ask, about the story.

Here is a simple knee scar, flat, unassuming, but wide and interrupted by the white pinpoints of suture marks. The scar is right over the kneecap, and it intrigues me. I ask its owner about its origin.

It was a rainy summer day, and his family was hurrying to climb the hill from their vacation cabin and get into their car. He was hurrying to catch up to his father, who was going up the hill, but his foot missed the step. He slipped and drove his knee into a sharp concrete edge. His kneecap was covered with blood.

He remembered looking into the deep laceration as the doctor cleaned it, seeing the white bone, the yellow tendon, the red muscle. The doctor put in seven stitches. "See, here are the scars."

A middle-aged woman has a long gray scar on her chest. I ask about her scar story, and she tells me the heart surgery went well, but the scar now has a painful life of its own. There is a constant pulling in and under it. A sensitive scar, this one is linked to the splitting of bone and the invasion of her chest cavity. The scar's story is never far below the surface, its pain always reminding her of its presence.

Scar watchers find scars everywhere.

An American with a small circular scar remembers. He was selling ice cream and had an argument with a customer over the amount of change. Ten minutes later the customer returned with a loaded gun and shot him in the thigh. The scar is tiny but full of anger, deep and unreasonable. It aches constantly as an uncivilized reminder of our times.

West African scars are masterpieces. I remember seeing the unique scars of each tribe, the ritualized scar tattoos. Some tribes scarify by burning; others cut or poke needles into back or chest. The marks are for life. A Bassa man can never forget who he is and where he came from; it is written in indelible white ink on his body.

Scars form because all healing is a combination of cell repair and sclerosis (from the Greek *skleros*, to dry or harden). Cells of more specialized and sophisticated tissues, such as the brain or heart, are less able to regenerate; these tissues must patch themselves solely with protein formed by scar cells.

Health professionals who are scar watchers are often very familiar with scars. We call them by name. The long, downward slanting scar below the right rib cage means gallbladder surgery. The small, right lower quadrant abdominal incision is from an appendectomy. The vertical midabdominal incision probably means a laparotomy; the vertical, lower abdominal scar an old C-section. The small circular scar

below the Adam's apple suggests tracheotomy; a long, hor-
izontal scar low in the neck may have been thyroid surgery.

Other scars tell stories of teenage acne, a car accident, a
slip on ice, a tooth through the lower lip of a child.

Inner scars tell subtler stories. An old heart attack requires
an EKG to reveal its existence. A paralyzed right leg suggests a scar in the left side of the brain, but only the CT scan
will show it to the scar watcher.

A long history of drinking and abnormal liver function
tests predict the usual story of liver scarring called cirrho-
sis, but only a liver needle biopsy will confirm it.

Why watch scars? Because they speak of wounds common to us all, wounds we must heal as fleshly creatures. Because scars point more deeply than themselves to our ways
of life, habits, and cultural practices, even our mistakes.

Children remember their scars; we adults must remember ours. Scars are lessons for us—old hurts we may be able
to avoid in the future, ways we shouldn't go. Scars remind
us we are liable to bleed if we put ourselves somewhere we
shouldn't. They are like palpable reminders of the frailties,
even the sins, of the body.

Perhaps we watch scars and show them to each other because they teach us that which we cannot afford to forget.

Part Three

Facing Death's Mystery

9

When CPR Becomes Futile

A Case that Went Both Ways

This is a true story about a patient of mine named Sally. She noticed it first at Thanksgiving: the shortness of breath, the heaviness, the swollen legs, the "weight" on the lung under the mastectomy scar. Although Sally was first my friend (I was eating pumpkin pie at her house that day), she became my patient. Her chest x ray showed a massive pleural effusion; I admitted her to the hospital, ordered a pleural biopsy (which showed malignancy), and had the chest surgeons perform pleural sclerosis to prevent future fluid accumulations.

The bone scan was also positive. Chemotherapy and hormonal therapy were instituted, and Sally became an official cancer patient. As her primary care physician, I saw her every month and observed the effects of her disease and treatment: dry and painful mouth, dry skin, pain in the hip, pain in the chest wall, shortness of breath, swollen legs, fatigue. These were the miseries she carried with her for the rest of her life. They varied only in degree. She suffered.

Three years passed, and although the cancer's progress was checked, she developed congestive heart failure and diabetes. Her visits became more frequent and were often urgent. As an ethicist, I knew I should discuss terminal care with her. As her friend and physician, I found this discussion extremely difficult. I knew the theory: Frame the end-of-life issues, arrange a consistent management plan which respects the patient's wishes, document the conversation in the chart. But in practice I was invested in keeping her alive, and she always deferred decisions to the hands of God.

Let me stop here to tell the moral of the story early. This patient received cancer treatment which prolonged her life. My medical management of Sally's diabetes and congestive heart failure was basically straightforward. Making the day-to-day ethical decisions in her care, however, was very complex. As she deteriorated, and as she suffered, the goals of treatment often blurred. Often it seemed that our treatment was futile in the Latin sense of the word: "leaky, vain, failing of the desired end." Should we keep going with chemotherapy? Is the goal years of survival, or months, or are we content with just days? Should we perform CPR when we know that if she survives she will still have painful, metastatic breast cancer?

Now the rest of the story. Sally had a sudden respiratory arrest (stopped breathing) several months before she died. She had elected to receive intensive care, but during the intubation (insertion of the ventilator tube) the anesthesiology resident couldn't find her trachea and broke one of her dental crowns. I happened to be at the bedside; I found the crown and put it in a bag. We finally got the tube in.

Amazingly, she survived the procedure. She was in the intensive care unit for a week but recovered and several weeks later appeared in my clinic. I felt terrible about the whole episode. She felt reasonably well (only three problems) and insisted on receiving aggressive care and CPR should she have another episode. She had been shopping the day before I saw her in the clinic, and she had spent the morning baking. Her dentist had repaired her broken tooth. She had made it to another spring. The rhubarb was almost ready to pull, and Sally would then make her famous rhubarb cake. Her fluid retention was better. "Look," she said, pointing toward her feet, "schoolgirl legs."

I was called to the hospital during her second and final code: cardiopulmonary arrest. I went to the bedside and watched as the residents tried without success, and I asked them to stop after several minutes of watching. They had been working on her for more than a half hour and couldn't get a sustained heartbeat. They did get occasional single beats.

The monitor showed that Sally's heart was still beating occasionally. I took her hand, and waited for the room to empty. "Sally," I whispered. "It's okay to go. It's okay to go." I turned off the monitor and kept my hand on her pulse. I felt an occasional beat for what seemed the longest time. "It's okay to go home now, to go home to the Lord," I said, stroking her forehead.

Finally, her heart stopped. I cried for a minute or two and then called her family. Sally wanted to donate her body to science, but too many Wisconsin cheeses, pies, and cakes of all kinds had made her too stout for the anatomy lab. I went to her autopsy, however, and saw how diseased her heart was (she had both ischemic cardiomyopathy and adriamycin [chemotherapy] cardiomyopathy). The myocardium was paper thin and flaccid. I saw the cancer in the pleura, scarred and quiescent. I saw her brain, glistening and free of metastases.

And I wondered: What part of Sally's care was effective? What did I do that was futile? In particular, was her last code futile, and should I have vetoed her request to be coded (receive CPR)?

The Long View of Futility: Chasing the Wind

> The Author: Solomon of Jerusalem, Kind David's son, "The Preacher."
> In my opinion, nothing is worthwhile; everything is futile. For what does a man get for all his hard work? . . .
> I, the Preacher, was king of Israel, living in Jerusalem. And I applied myself to search for understanding about everything in the universe. I discovered that the lot of man, which God has dealt to him, is not a happy one. It is all foolishness, chasing the wind. What is wrong cannot be righted; it is water over the dam; and there is no use thinking of what might have been.
> I said to myself, "Look, I am better educated than any of the kings before me in Jerusalem. I have greater wisdom and knowledge." So I worked hard to be wise instead of foolish—but now I realize that even this was like chasing the wind. For the more my wisdom, the more my grief; to increase knowledge only increases distress (Eccles. 1:1–3, 12–18 TLB).

The writer of Ecclesiastes notes that from an eternal perspective, our materialistic gathering of knowledge and possessions is futile. We die and our possessions will be passed to others (and may even be squandered if they are foolish or profligate). Dust to dust, ashes to ashes, we are in many ways like water over the dam. We can carve out the river channel with our lives, but then we have to move on and can never go back in our human bodies.

Even education does not permanently change the fundamental human situation. While education may make us more civil or sophisticated, improve our standard of living, and increase our capacity for enjoying literature and the other arts, it cannot grant us life. Medicine can do much, but we cannot slash and suture our way to eternal life. In the sense of the Alpha and Omega, the span of a human life is vanishingly short.

Another passage, Ecclesiastes 12:1, 5, is even more compelling: "Remember your Creator in the days of your youth, before the days of trouble come and the years approach when you will say, I find no pleasure in them". . . . Then man goes to his eternal home and mourners go about the streets."

In this beautiful but sobering section we are reminded again of our own timelines. The time to serve God is in the days of our vigor and youth; later years may find us infirm and even struggling to survive. For example, Sally's autopsy showed that her ongoing survival was actually a moment-by-moment struggle: Her heart was a failing pump.

The realistic view of aging is that while many aged people are vigorous and productive, growing old also usually involves illness and loss. Bodily functions are impaired, family members and friends die, and chronic diseases emerge. Still, caregivers can improve the day-to-day aspects of patients' lives, work with them to tailor treatment plans which honor their wishes, and love and comfort them when the days of trouble come and the sun and the stars grow dark.

When Is It Reasonable to Forego Aggressive Treatment?

Comfort and support are never futile, but sometimes aggressive medical treatment is futile. Futility is neither the impossible nor the implausible. Rather, as Schneiderman et al point out, "a futile action is one that cannot achieve the goals of the action, no matter how often repeated. The likelihood of failure may be predictable because it is inherent in the action proposed, and it may become immediately obvious or may become apparent only after many failed attempts . . . we propose that . . . 'futile' be used to describe any effort to achieve a result that is possible but that reasoning or experience suggests is highly improbable and that cannot be systematically reproduced."[1] For example, two successes achieved against a background of hundreds of failures do not change the reality that the treatment is futile. Note that this definition suits aggressive medical treatment, not hospice care or comfort measures.[2]

Futile treatments are those which offer no benefit, which do more harm than good, or which in the doctor's, and the patient's judgment could not realistically achieve the goals of treatment. Patients do not have the inherent right to futile treatment. However, futility judgments are inherently moral judgments as well as clinical judgments. They should not be made unilaterally by the physician but should involve the patient, or the patient's family, because the patient is involved in the process of treatment.

If treatments offer absolutely no possibility of success, the doctor alone can decide, because such treatments are not futile, they are impossible. But in the issue of futility—that is, related to reasonably achieving the mutually agreed on goals of treatment—the patient needs a say.

Let's get back to Sally's case. Was resuscitation futile? Some authors suggest that a success rate of less than 5 percent indicates that attempts at resuscitation could be futile. But let's examine the data. Cardiopulmonary resuscitation is attempted in one-third of those who die in American hospitals. Two-thirds are do-not-resuscitate or DNR patients. For every 100 patients who are coded, thirty survive the initial resuscitation effort; ten of the survivors leave the hospital; eight of these individuals will be alive six months later, and 6 will be alive five years later. Half of those who receive CPR are over age sixty-five. The majority of the survivors remember nothing about the experience except a sore chest on awakening. Most long-term survivors resume their previous activity, but almost half decide to forego CPR in the future. On average 2 percent of the survivors will be left in the persistent vegetative state.[3]

As these data suggest, long-term survivors of cardiopulmonary arrest have run a daunting biological gauntlet. Full recovery from cardiopulmonary arrest is a test of the responsiveness of the cardiopulmonary system, the tolerance of the brain to global ischemia, and the severity of the underlying illness. The potluck nature of such survival makes it difficult to know beforehand whether a given patient is an ideal candidate for CPR. As Youngner has pointed out, it may not be possible to identify those individual patients for whom resuscitation will certainly be futile. The best we can do is identify broad categories of patients in whom long-term survival after CPR is highly unlikely.[4]

Using Data to Help Patients Decide: Cancer and Age as an Example

Many studies have shown that groups of patients with cancer experience poor outcomes after CPR. In the study by Taffet et al none of the eighty-nine cancer patients lived to discharge (leave the hospital).[5] Multivariate analysis revealed that other predictors of survival to discharge included the presence of a witness at the time of the arrest, the number of medication doses given during the resuscitation, and age. The authors note that despite studies which suggest that age is not an important determinant of long-term survival after resuscitation, "it is our clinical impression that a majority of our geriatric patients were not living to discharge after CPR." This clinical hypothesis led to their study and to their most controversial finding: none of the sixty-eight patients over age seventy who received CPR survived to discharge. Murphy has reported similar results.[6]

Most studies find no statistical age bias in DNR (do-not-resuscitate) status, number of witnessed arrests, hospital location, or vigor of resuscitation. The number of listed di-

agnoses, used as a crude index of severity of illness, is usually significantly higher in those over seventy, although the
prevalence of cancer is no different. When the impact of increased age on survival was evaluated while controlling for
the estimate of severity of illness, age alone persists as a significant variable.

Although it is difficult to accurately assess mental function from chart review (studies based on information in hospital medical records), poor neurologic recovery after CPR
appeared to be a problem for Taffet's patients over age seventy, with only four of twenty-two patients ever regaining
orientation to person. To corroborate their findings, the authors examined eight other similar studies and found that
age seventy years or greater was significantly associated with
not living to discharge after CPR.

This conclusion must be balanced against the Office of
Technology Assessment's (OTA) extensive review of CPR in
the elderly.[7] The OTA report cites eight studies (three of which
are also cited by Taffet et al) to support the conclusion that
age alone is *not* a good predictor of the long-term outcome
of resuscitation. According to the OTA, however, some of
these studies show "that elderly patients as a group have
somewhat poorer outcomes than younger patients but that
the poorer outcomes in elderly patients reflect the higher
prevalence of multiple diseases in these patients. Although
the likelihood of multiple diseases increases with age, any
particular older individual may not be affected." For their
part, the authors of the present study do not recommend setting age limits for CPR. They recognize their findings apply
to the population of sick, aged, male Veteran's Administration (VA) patients and may not be applicable to other pop-
ulations, other settings, or any given patient, like Sally.

Thus, while the authors of the OTA document and other
studies seem to arrive at different conclusions based on similar data, the actual disagreement is over the potential use

of age or disease as a single marker for the actual chances for survival to discharge after CPR.

In practice, we find that a previously healthy elderly person has as good or better chance of surviving resuscitation as a chronically ill young person. Actually, many of us are more troubled by the unsuccessful resuscitation of patients—young or old—who seem to be at the end of their lives. We sometimes try to resusitate patients who are dying a natural death.

We as caregivers need to realistically discuss this issue with our patients.[8] These discussions should occur in a quiet environment, the language should be simple, questions should be encouraged, understanding should be checked, and physicians should strive to improve their communication skills in this regard. This is easier said than done; as I noted, in Sally's case these discussions were difficult.

Speaking with Patients about Foregoing CPR

Since we recognize that patients may well choose to have their families and friends surround them at the time of death rather than the code team, we may in the course of these discussions recommend that a patient consider foregoing CPR because the chance for meaningful survival is low. Furthermore, we might use the data of Taffet et al and others to point out that the burden of CPR may be high: after initial resuscitation, patients are usually cared for in an ICU or critical care unit (CCU) with the high technology and high cost attendant to such settings, and even so, more than two-thirds will still die.

This information may be significant to patients when combined with survival data. In Taffet's studies, all of the twenty-two elderly patients who survived CPR initially and were alive at twenty-four hours, went to the ICU and then died, as did 102 of 124 younger patients.

Presenting these facts will not remove the difficulties, am-
biguities, or symbolic and emotional facets of decisions to
forego resuscitative technologies. But they can provide physicians, patients, and families with a valuable and morally rel-
evant basis for initial discussions. These discussions are important. If the patient is unable
to participate and if a family member is not available, then
another appropriate person should be involved in the conversations. Herein is the appropriate use of age or cancer
diagnosis: the advanced age or chronic illness of a hospitalized patient should at least prompt ongoing discussion
about the use of lifesaving technologies including CPR.

While many researchers acknowledge that in some cases
it will be unclear when a patient's medical condition would
make CPR absolutely futile, most use metastatic cancer as
an example of such a condition. But what about patients
like Sally? The work of Taffet et al needs to be extended,
but suppose that other large studies of hospitalized Veteran's
Administration patients document survival to discharge of
less than 2 percent among men over seventy. Will the age of
hospitalized male veterans then become the criterion for a
condition for which CPR has been shown not to be effective? The problem with this approach is that a particular elderly person may not be affected by multiple diseases. This
person may survive CPR, and just as importantly, may wish
to try surviving CPR.

Conclusion

Contrary to what many health professionals and members of the public believe, CPR is not the norm in American
hospitals; most patients (two-thirds) choose to forego resuscitation, and many others would choose to do so if ap-
propriately informed. Studies can enable physicians to make
more informed recommendations to patients and families
about resuscitation. Advanced age or a diagnosis of cancer

can be clinical characteristics which trigger such discussions and under certain circumstances may predict poor long-term survival after CPR.

Age or cancer per se, however, should not preclude patients from receiving CPR. CPR should not be withheld from individual patients based solely on the physician's unilateral assessment of futility. Patients like Sally might benefit from resuscitation if it offers a chance to enjoy the spring sunshine one more time. But when treatment becomes futile— when the monitor shows an occasional beat but there is no physiologic response—further efforts are vain. May God grant us as patients and caregivers discernment so that together we might avoid striving after the wind.

10

In Due Season

Before the widespread use of modern medical technology, the due season for death was obvious and "natural"; people just died. Fortunately, this is no longer the case. Our current ability to sustain life is a blessing to be used wisely in the care of the sick. Unfortunately, along with our enhanced technologic power we don't seem to have gained better judgment. With increasing ability to be invasive we are not more gentle; with dramatic power to work with life we do not have a better understanding about the nature of life itself. We seem to need to re-learn how to give comfort and care, and to know when aggressive treatment is futile.

If today's doctors can "prevent" the immediacy of death, if our technology can temporarily delay death, then someone must decide wisely on the due season for death. In the midst of tubes, lines, and powerful pressor (blood-pressure elevating) drugs, can we die when it is really our time?

Caregiver Competence and Wisdom

One modern philosopher has discussed the tension between the scientific and nonscientific community which causes the scientific to view ethical concerns as the result of latent antiscientific feeling. As a clinician I sense that tension; "abstract" philosophic concerns seem out of touch with what I do day to day. However, I have come to appreciate what has been called the inescapability of moral decisions; I do not make solely technologic decisions. The decision to put a patient who is hypoxic and hypotensive in the intensive care unit involves a mixture of medical indications *and* patient preferences *and* doctor-patient-family communication *and* my own internal value system as a Christian physician.

The public perceives medical personnel to be technically competent; this is fortunate for, as Pellegrino has stated, compassion without competence is a moral fraud and a betrayal of patient trust.[1] Technology, then, as I have pointed out in the modern Job story, is not the problem; I want to make this point clear. Technology can be used for good; we can use it to benefit patients. The problem comes in the wise and appropriate use of technology, in the ethical decision-making process of employing it. This process, which I will discuss in detail, boils down to a series of basic questions: Can technology prolong life? Yes. Then can doctors themselves and the technicians prolong life? Yes. Eternally? No. Ought they, then, always to prolong life? I would argue, no.

Can Caregivers Prolong Life?

Most of us can name patients who would be dead except for our efforts. We don't want to exaggerate our importance; we state the practical truth, that medicine is an important factor in saving some lives. Preventive medicine saves lives, as does intensive care medicine.

At the bedside or in the clinic I have often marveled at the tenacity of human life when aided by appropriate technology. For example:

Case 1: A sixty-five-year-old woman was transferred to the CCU with an inferior wall myocardial infarction. She developed a bradycardia and despite medication went into asystole. She was intubated, a Swan-Ganz pacing catheter was placed in her right ventricle, and she was treated with a host of drugs and multiple cardioversions for runs of ventricular fibrillation and ventricular tachycardia. After an hour she suddenly had a final run of ventricular tachycardia, which converted to sinus tachycardia. Since she had effective CPR throughout the code, she had minimal brain anoxia. She went home, fully oriented and able to converse normally and care for herself.

Case 2: A twenty-year-old man noticed a lump in his neck. Examination revealed a lymph node, which on biopsy was Hodgkin's disease. It had spread to several deeper nodes. He received radiation therapy and is alive and disease-free five years later.

Case 3: A sixty-five-year-old woman with severe emphysema was given the flu and pneumonia vaccines. She was well the next spring in spite of the severe influenza epidemic which ravaged the community.

Case 4: An African mother was given tetanus antitoxoid. Her next child did not develop neonatal tetanus, unlike the previous child who died of it.

Case 5: A ten-year-old boy developed right-lower-quadrant pain. He had an uneventful appendectomy.

These five cases reveal that modern medical techniques can prolong lives. In case 1, ICU care leads to the complete resuscitation of a woman who would have been declared dead just decades ago. Case 2 illustrates the effective treatment available for some types of cancer. Before radiation therapy, surgery alone probably would not have saved this patient's life. Cases 3 and 4 show the results of vaccines which can protect both the elderly and the unborn. Case 5 is a young boy who might have died a century ago and probably would have died five centuries ago.

Doctors and their techniques, then, can prolong life. Moreover, doctors are bound by long moral and professional tradition to do so. Kass puts it succinctly:

> To protect life, to maintain and support it, to restore it to wholeness, and certainly not to destroy it is the common principle [in medicine]. To be sure, this principle gets outside support from religious teachings . . . but one sees it can be derived from the inner meaning of medicine itself."[2]

If our technology enables us to save lives and our profession's inner meaning is found in support of life, we will be strongly biased toward life and "err on the side of life," in Dr. C. Everett Koop's words. Health professionals will be generally in favor of life-sustaining measures in most cases. Caregivers will sometimes find it difficult to "allow" dying patients to die, and we will often find it difficult to know our part in the timing of death. If we begin and continue life support in some patients we may merely delay the dying process; if we fail to start or if we withdraw life support, we face the problem of having potentially hastened death. We find this same balance, between the inevitability of physical death and the joy of physical life, in our own tradition.

We are of Adam, we have eaten of the fruit of the tree in the center of the garden, and we shall surely die. Death is not only for the poor (Luke 12:20; 1 Tim. 6:7); all are dust (Gen. 3:19). This realistic view of humans, which is supported by other passages (Ps. 90:3–4; Job 7:1, 21; 2 Sam. 14:14; Rom. 5:12; 1 Peter 1:24), is balanced by the important principle of the high value of physical human life (Gen.

4:9–12; 9:5–6; Exod. 20:13; Ps. 26:9; 139:16; Matt. 6:22–27).

At best, even with our most powerful technology, we cannot gain final power over death. Only Jesus has gained that victory (1 Cor. 15:26). However, God gives extension of physical life to certain people: Hezekiah in 2 Kings 20:5–6; Elijah's landlady's son in 1 Kings 17:21–23; a centurion's daughter in Luke 8:49–55; and Lazarus in John 11:38–44). In each of these cases, people were restored to health, not an extended period of suffering or prolonged dying. It follows that Jesus would allow caregivers and their technologies to extend physical life as well. While we cannot have final power over death, we can achieve temporary (as measured in years) power over death. However, we sometimes

Withholding or Withdrawing Life-Prolonging Medical Treatment

Summary of AMA Opinions from 1986–93

1. The social commitment of the physician is to sustain life and relieve suffering. Where the performance of one duty conflicts with the other, the choice of the patient, or his family or legal representative if the patient is incompetent to act in his own behalf, should prevail. In the absence of the patient's choice or an authorized proxy, the physician must act in the best interests of the patient.

2. For humane reasons, with informed consent, a physician may do what is medically necessary to alleviate severe pain, or cease or omit treatment to permit a terminally ill patient whose death is imminent to die. However, he should not intentionally cause

From Council on Ethical Judicial Afairs of the AMA. "Decisions Near the End of Life," *Journal of the American Medical Association* 267 (1992): 2229–33.

risk extending suffering or prolonging dying. Herein lies the doctor's dilemma, and the patient's, too.

The American Medical Association's Response

Each time the members of the AMA Judicial Council publish guidelines (below) for the withholding or withdrawal of life-prolonging treatment, they are careful to specify that the physician is committed to sustaining life and relieving suffering and that the physician should not intentionally cause death. The present guidelines allow for (but do not mandate) the withholding or withdrawal of medication, artificial respiration, nutrition and hydration in terminally ill or irreversibly comatose patients. The language is more spe-

---

death. In deciding whether the administration of potentially life-prolonging medical treatment is in the best interests of the patient who is incompetent to act in his own behalf, the physician should determine what the possibility is for extending life under humane and comfortable conditions and what are the prior expressed wishes of the patient and attitudes of the family or those who have responsibility for the custody of the patient.

3. Even if death is not imminent but a patient's coma is beyond doubt irreversible, and there are adequate safeguards to confirm the accuracy of the diagnosis and with the concurrence of those who have responsibility for the care of the patient, it is not unethical to discontinue all means of life-prolonging medical treatment.

4. Life-prolonging medical treatment includes medication and artificially or technologically supplied respiration, nutrition, or hydration. In treating a terminally ill or irreversibly comatose patient, the physician should determine whether the benefits of treatment outweigh its burdens. At all times, the dignity of the patient should be maintained.

cific than in previous guidelines, which did not address the individual technologies which could be withdrawn. A major article in the *New England Journal of Medicine* reached a similar conclusion but admitted that "few topics in medicine are more complicated, more controversial, and more emotionally charged than treatment of the hopelessly ill. Technology competes with compassion, legal precedent lags, and controversy is inevitable."[3]

Conclusion

Back to the bedside, and toward a difficult but honest conclusion: The exact point at which technology becomes inappropriate differs for each patient, because each of us has a different due season. I hope my physician gathers the medical facts, discerns my preferences for life-sustaining measures, and acts benevolently toward me, preserving my life, controlling my pain. However, I also hope she will judge objectively and compassionately when not to employ technologic power to prolong my life (and thus when to "allow" my death).

I realize this requires me to trust my physician to be able to let me die in my due season. I would let her know I wish and expect her to be biased toward life; that is the nature of her profession, after all. I would want her to be technologically competent, but there is a lot of "technology" I wouldn't necessarily want her to use on me. When the time comes, the use of that technology would depend on her clinical judgment. The scenario I propose rests on the presumption that my physician is looking out for my well-being despite economic or cultural pressures to do otherwise. It presumes that caregivers treat others as if we were treating ourselves. And it admits that for each of us there is still a time to die.

Back to the bedside again. I have shared stories with other physicians about the timing of death. Some patients seem to be able to live to attend that wedding, make it to Christmas, see the granddaughter born, resolve a family conflict. I have seen skilled physicians anticipate and treat crisis after crisis and somehow manage to "pull the patient through." I stand in awe of the mystery of physical life and physical death. But still there is a time for death.

At the point when the struggle is futile it would seem appropriate to admit the patient's time has come and bring our technology back into line with this reality to back off. Using the bodies of our patients to fight back the shadow of death is a hopeless and macabre struggle.

11

In the Valley of the Shadow

Nancy Cruzan and PVS

On the night of January 11, 1983, a twenty-four-year-old woman named Nancy Beth Cruzan lost control of her car on a rural road in Missouri. Her car turned over, and when the paramedics arrived she was lying face down and was not breathing. She had sustained brain trauma and her brain had also been without oxygen for a significant period of time. Damage to the brain usually results after four to six minutes without oxygen, and it was later estimated by her physicians that Nancy Cruzan's brain had been without oxygen for twelve to fourteen minutes before paramedics began the resuscitation effort. Resuscitation continued while Ms. Cruzan was being rushed to the hospital intensive care unit. Months later, she was diagnosed as being in the persistent vegetative state. PVS is not the same as brain death. Brain death requires the death of the whole brain, including the brain stem. A patient with PVS has lost his or her cortex;

the patient is not brain dead. A patient's brain stem often survives the lack of oxygen, even if the cortex is irreversibly destroyed. However, less than twenty-five years ago this patient would have died without tube feeding and other treatments. Such a patient is not dead, but is in the "valley of the shadow."

What are the clinical consequences of this cortical damage? The medical problem of persistent vegetative state after brain damage was first described by Bryan Jennett and Fred Plum in *The Lancet* on April 1, 1972.[1] They noted that once past the acute stage of coma, these patients are neither unconscious nor in coma in the usual sense of the terms. For a week these patients are in coma. Their eyes are closed, and they can't be aroused. Two or three weeks after the injury, they open their eyes; they have periods when they rest with their eyes open; at other times they seem to sleep. Their eyes are open and may blink, but they do not focus; these patients are awake but not aware.

They may have a grasp reflex, and chewing and teeth grinding are common. Most patients are silent, but some may groan. Over time, PVS patients develop contractures of their limbs from the lack of purposeful movement. Under the microscope, most patients' brains show extensive cortical destruction, but there is a small group which may have more localized damage.

Jennett and Plum proposed the persistent vegetative state as a name for the syndrome for several reasons. *Vegetate* means to live a merely physical life devoid of intellectual activity or social intercourse, and *vegetative* describes an organic body capable of growth and development but devoid of sensation or thought. *Persistent* means ongoing without change. Jennett and Plum said that the essential component of this syndrome called persistent vegetative state, or PVS, was the absence of any adaptive response to the external environment, and the absence of any evidence of a functioning mind which is either receiving or projecting information, in a patient who has long periods of wakefulness.

Nancy Cruzan's parents asked to have her feeding tube removed and a Missouri state hospital declined to remove the tube without a court order. A Missouri trial court found that Cruzan had previously had conversations with a friend in which she expressed her wish not to live unless she could live "at least halfway normally." It authorized the removal of a tube. But the Missouri Supreme Court, by a 4–3 vote reversed this decision, arguing that clear and convincing evidence was needed. The United States Supreme Court, by a 5–4 decision, upheld the Missouri Supreme Court. In *Cruzan*, the Court said that where the evidence of a patient's wishes is unclear, a state may assert its interest in the protection of human life by requiring that tube feeding continue. Such a state requirement does not violate the United States Constitution. After former co-workers of Cruzan testified they recalled her saying she would never want to live "like a vegetable," a state judge ruled that clear and convincing evidence did exist, and he gave permission on December 14, 1990, to remove the tube. Nancy Cruzan died twelve days later.

Principles and Issues

Concerns over sanctity of life, autonomy and human dignity, quality of life, medical futility, medical treatment versus supportive care, legal precedents, cost, and symbolic and psychological concerns are involved in arguments and decisions about treatment of patients with PVS, who live in the "valley of the shadow."

Sanctity of Life

Sanctity of life is the ethical principle that human life has inestimable value. This principle holds that an individual human life is "absolutely unique, inviolable, irreplaceable, noninterchangeable, not substitutable, and not meldable with other lives."[2] Thus, the value of a human life does not consist in its worth to anybody but is intrinsic; there can be no degrees of value and no comparison of the value of different individuals' lives, regardless of their medical or social condition.

Autonomy and Human Dignity

Autonomy is the right to self-determination. This ethical principle is expressed in health care in the legal doctrine and clinical practice of informed consent. Competent patients have the right to refuse treatment, even life-sustaining treatment. The refusal of such treatment is not suicide but instead may promote the patient's own interests. For example, a patient dying of severe breast cancer may refuse experimental chemotherapy and a person with pancreatic cancer may refuse surgery, both for reasons of living for a shorter time but with (probably) better function. Advance directives in the form of written or verbal statements regarding treatment, living wills, or durable powers of attorney are legitimate expressions of autonomy in the event of future incompetence. Human dignity in health care is reflected in respectful treatment; patients are worthy of esteem and honor.

Quality of Life

To define quality-of-life judgments we must say they are, by necessity, subjective evaluations by an onlooker about another's life, when the patient can't make such an evaluation or express it because of mental incapacity.[3] They are not first-person assessments. If an individual considers his or her life to be of little value, that is, by definition, an autonomous expression and not a quality-of-life judgment. It is only in the setting of incompetence that onlookers can "judge" the quality of another's life—by necessity when the other cannot speak for himself or herself. The inherent problem of subjectivity makes quality of life judgments risky at best. Nonetheless, this issue is a common one for many caregivers.

Medical Futility

Medical futility is difficult to define, for some physicians and patients would consider treatments which do not return patients to a certain quality of life to be futile; other guidelines contain a more rigorous and circumscribed view of medical futility. The physician's unilateral assessment of the benefit of treatment is not sufficient to render a treatment futile. The Hastings Center guidelines, for example, note that treatments can be declared medically futile only when they will clearly fail to achieve a physiological objective (for example, the treatment would not eliminate a widespread cancer), and that even such treatments can be provided if the patient or surrogate requests them.

Medical Treatment versus Supportive Care

Important differences exist between medical treatment and supportive care. Medical treatment is the treatment provided by physicians and other health professionals aimed at accomplishing the goals of medical practice. Supportive care is the care provided by care givers—family members, nurses' aides, other health professionals—aimed at providing human comforts even to the dying patient. Caregivers should continue to provide it. But they are not obligated to provide general medical treatment or specialized life-sustaining treatment to every patient just because such technology is available. Medical treatments can and sometimes should be withdrawn from patients. Since no medical procedure can determine the conditions for its own use, the lessons of clinical experience or the weight of moral considerations may make its use inappropriate in a given case. The problem is, determining when and if to stop is not as easy and clear as this argument suggests.

Legal Precedents

The courts have consistently considered tube feeding to be similar to respirators, dialysis machines, antibiotics, and chemotherapy; legal decisions have allowed the withdrawal of tube feeding by competent patients or their surrogates. In *Cruzan v. Director*, several of the justices noted that the withdrawal of feeding is akin to the withdrawal of medical treatment.

Cost

Specific data on the cost of providing nutritional support and hydration are difficult to obtain, since many patients who require these supports have other medical problems and expenses as well. Even if the expense is considerable, some would argue that this expenditure is not "a morally troubling misallocation of societal resources" and that given the current push to reduce health-care costs, especially long-term nursing care, society should be very cautious lest routine withdrawal of nutritional support be seen as a means of cost containment. The costs of maintaining these patients varies by state, institution, and support system, but range between $25,000 and $100,000 a year.

Emotional Concerns

Some people feel a moral repugnance or revulsion at the thought of withdrawing tube feeding from patients who cannot feed themselves. Feeding has symbolic importance in every society, including our own. The question is whether symbolic issues are important because they are symbolic or symbolic because they are important. Food is also emotionally important because of its prominence in social gatherings and in religious traditions (Christian communion and

Jewish Seder). So stopping feeding seems more significant, for example, than stopping dialysis.

Arguments: Pro and Con

The principles and concepts discussed above are directly applied in arguments about tube feeding. Half a dozen arguments can be made in favor of withdrawal of feeding, and half a dozen can be made against withdrawal of feeding. Some of the same arguments can be made for or against the withdrawal of ventilators or dialysis. Tube feeding withdrawal is, however, a more poignant issue in many cases because the patient is in "the valley of the shadow" and precisely for that reason can't eat. Or the patient is like Cardinal Jackson, seemingly at the end of life, but still able to hang on.

Arguments for Withdrawal of Tube Feeding

Those who argue for withdrawal of tube feeding make the arguments outlined below.

1. When the neurologic prognosis for functional recovery is grim, such as in persistent vegetative state, and the best clinical judgment is that the situation is irreversible, continued feeding with little hope of the benefit of functional return imposes severe burdens on patient and family. Feeding then becomes only a prolongation of the dying process.
2. There is no technological imperative to use a feeding tube; there is no obligation to use nutritional support in every patient just because this technology is available. The rights of the patient outweigh the rights of the tube.
3. If a tube can never be removed, the ability to perform therapeutic "trials" of tube feeding is impaired. There will be a high up-front barrier to the use of feeding

tubes, and some patients who might benefit from nutritional support will not receive a trial because they or their families will be reluctant to begin something which can never be stopped. Actually, more lives would be saved in the long run if most or all patients were offered a short trial of feeding, and if feeding were withdrawn from a few patients rather than withheld from many patients.

4. The removal of tube feeding is no different from the removal of other technologic support, including the withdrawal of a respirator, dialysis, or antibiotics. Assistance with failing pulmonary function or renal function is as vital to life as assistance with gastrointestinal function. Which, after all, is more immediately critical to life: air or water?

5. While all living patients need food, they do not all need feeding tubes. The need for such a tube may imply an illness which may and should precede a natural death. While food can be offered by spoon or syringe, there is no ethical obligation to insert a tube. As Dr. Ed Payne suggests, physicians can make sure that if they withdraw or withhold tube feeding they continue to offer food in the traditional and noninvasive sense, i.e., by mouth.[4] Others have argued that any treatment that appears to deny the reality of impending death or extreme disability is undignified.

6. The argument for widespread and nondiscriminatory tube feeding in all cases is based on emotional rather than ethical reasons.

Arguments against Withdrawal of Tube Feeding

Those against withdrawal of tube feeding in most or all clinical situations make the following arguments.

1. Denial of food and fluids is physiologically final in a way that withdrawal of other treatments is not. In other words, nutritional support and hydration are never or rarely physiologically futile. Calories delivered to the digestive tract do nourish in almost all cases. Some say this method of dying may be unpleasant, especially if the patient suffers the feelings of dehydration or hunger.

2. As a corollary, the withdrawal of food and fluids causes death uniformly in any creature, regardless of health. There is a complete and total clinical linkage between the withdrawal of this particular therapy and the patient's death, if they are really unable to eat, like Nancy Cruzan.

3. There will be negative effects on the integrity of caregivers if a policy of withdrawing tube feeding is implemented, especially if feeding is withdrawn for financial reasons. Physicians may find themselves on the ledge of a slippery slope and may be unable to avoid performing active euthanasia. After all, if the intent of tube feeding withdrawal is to bring death in ten to fourteen days, why not give the lethal injection and avoid the prolonged dehydration period?

4. The provision of nutritional support is supportive care, not technology, or at least not merely high technology.

5. An individual's inability to feed himself or herself should not mean we decide not to feed him; in fact, it should mean just the opposite.

6. The emotional aspect of feeding is important because it embodies our deeply held moral and social instincts. Our repugnance to withdrawing or withholding feeding is protective; feeding may be our minimal bottom-line human obligation to other persons, even those who are irreversibly or terminally ill.

Toward a Position—
The Christian Medical-Dental Society
Position Paper on Tube Feeding

How do we resolve this dilemma of the care of patients who are in the shadow of death and require artificial feeding?

Members of the CMDS ethics committee struggled to put together a position statement. As the CMDS tube-feeding statement shows, the society agrees on the basic principles of providing feeding to vulnerable patients. The statement was passed unanimously by the society leadership. As the asterisk shows, we did not, however, finish discussion or deliberations on our position regarding the withdrawal of nutrition and hydration *in coma or persistent vegetative state.* The statement did not specifically address the situation of patients like Nancy Cruzan. That is a problem with being in the shadow—much is uncertain. But in the second paragraph we acknowledge that sometimes artificial feeding can prolong dying.

The Withholding or Withdrawing of Nutrition and Hydration

The primary goal of the Christian clinical ethic is to provide compassionate medical care to all human beings. We recognize that nutritional support is both a universal human biologic requirement and a fundamental demonstration of human caring. Because we believe there should be a basic covenant between all of us to care for those who are incapacitated, we are committed to the provision of food and water to those who cannot feed themselves.

In exceptional cases, tube feeding may actually result in increased patient suffering during the dying process. Although we have a basic covenant to offer food and water to patients, we recognize that the provision of enteral or parenteral nutrition may not be indicated in patients who are clearly and irreversibly deteriorating, who are beyond a reasonable hope of recovery, and in whom death appears im-

minent. In such cases, it is ethically permissible to withhold
or withdraw nutrition and hydration, in full consideration
of patient and family wishes.

However, we believe that physicians, other health professionals, and health-care facilities should initiate and continue nutritional support and hydration when their patients
cannot feed themselves. We are concerned that demented,
severely retarded, and comatose* individuals are increasingly viewed as "useless mouths." (We reject this dehuman-
izing phrase.) Rather than encouraging physicians to withhold or withdraw such patients' food and water, we
encourage physicians to respond to God's call for improved
physical, social, and spiritual support of all vulnerable
human beings.

*The issue of the treatment of patients in coma or per-
sistent vegetative state (PVS) is part of the ongoing deliberations of the Ethics Commission and CMDS. A separate
statement on this problem is under discussion.

*Passed unanimously by the CMDS House of Delegates,
May 3, 1990, Toronto, Canada.*

Conclusion

In this chapter I have reviewed the medical condition of
PVS and outlined some of the various arguments in *Cruzan*.
This has not been a discussion of physician-assisted suicide
and euthanasia, which I oppose and on which CMDS has a
statement that makes its principles clear and its position
firm. But what do we do about our Nancy Cruzans?

This ethical issue merits continuing serious debate and
consideration by the public but especially by health-care
givers. Answers are not simple, but by considering the arguments on this issue and the basic principles, decision mak-
ers will be better served.

12

Cadaver Ethics

I know that my Redeemer lives, and that in the end he will stand upon the earth. And after my skin has been destroyed, yet in my flesh I will see God; I myself will see him with my own eyes—I, and not another. How my heart yearns within me! (Job 19:25–27).

The first and most obvious question we might ask is, Why should health professionals or caregivers concern themselves with "cadaver ethics"? After all, we have living patients with pressing problems. Every day, in the hospital or clinic, we face issues such as the withdrawal of life-sustaining treatment, the rational use of high technology, and the appropriate use of scarce resources. Given the needs of the living and the weighty nature of these dilemmas, we might ques-

Editor's note: This chapter is a revised version of the lecture Dr. Schiedermayer gives each year during the first day of dissection in the medical school anatomy course. During this course, a group of four students is assigned a cadaver to dissect; usually one student reads the dissection manual, one student performs the dissection, and the other two observe. Students are required to memorize the location and particular function of nerves, muscles, arteries, and major organ systems.

tion the clinical importance of cadaver ethics. After all, how can the dead be harmed? The subject might merit passing attention since medical students may have emotional problems in the cadaver lab, but counseling is available for such students. Why should the rest of us consider the issue?

Why Cadaver Ethics Are Important

I think some reflection is in order before students enter the lab, because I am convinced that what students think about the cadaver is an ethical issue of critical importance. The way students treat cadavers reveals much not only about the kind of doctors they become but about their view of the human being.

The dead body, while no longer a human presence, reminds us of the presence which was once utterly inseparable from it. The dead body, from a Christian standpoint, awaits the holy power of God. As the Scriptures say, although the skin may be destroyed, yet "in my flesh I will see God." We believe in the resurrection of the body and the life everlasting.

Studies reveal that health professional students' emotional reactions to the cadaver are significant. While a first-year medical student may understand the necessity of anatomical dissection for proper training, he or she may initially find the activity quite repulsive. One observer reports that his students wondered, "What if the relatives were to walk in? I feel as if I am abusing the family." "Did this guy knowingly consent to be dissected? Did he really know what we are going to do to him?" "I would never let this happen to my father—or myself."[1]

Some students are concerned with looking at the face, the eyes, the skin, the hands, or the genitals. Some experience, at least initially, troubling images; some have dreams; and some experience stress reactions and even interference with their own sexuality. The first encounter with one newly dead body is described most vividly by Richard Selzer:

> Dead, the body is somehow more solid, more massive. The shrink of dying is past. It is as though only moments before a wind had kept it aloft, and now, settled, it is only what it is, a mass, declaring itself, an ugly emphasis. Almost at once the skin changes color, from pink-highlighted yellow to gray-tinted blue. The eyes are open and lack-luster; something, a bright dust, has been blown away, leaving the globes smoky. And there is an absolute limpness. Hours later, the neck and limbs are drawn up into a semiflexion, in the attitude of one who had just received a blow to the solar plexus.
>   One has.[2]

The Problem of Mistreatment of Cadavers

What is a dead body? Let me start with the most practical observation. Whatever it is, the dead physical body has enough moral significance that certain actions toward it may constitute mistreatment. More than twenty years ago Congressman John Moss of California learned that dead bodies had been used by the department of transportation to measure the effectiveness of various crash protective devices in automobile collisions.[3] The cadavers came from the "willed body program," and family permission to use them in this manner had been secured wherever possible. The department of transportation noted that crash testing requires an insignificant number of bodies compared with the number needed for medical school dissection, and that the information gained from cadavers was critical to the design of better dummies. In their words, "Of all available surrogates for the human body, the cadaver possesses the greatest mechanical and geometrical similarity with the living person." No surprise!

Congressman Moss, incensed, noted that "the use of

human cadavers for vehicle safety research violates fundamental notions of morality and human dignity, and must therefore permanently be stopped." Most research was stopped. Some cadaver testing is still done, however, and is necessary to calibrate the crash dummies. My point here is straightforward: Society has an interest in how dead bodies are used, an interest which considers the unique benefit of their use versus the violence and mutilation required by that use. Using cadavers in crashes, or dropping them into empty elevator shafts to test leg fractures is somehow emotionally repugnant. So is medical dissection, but the difference is that in medical dissection, society sees that there is no good substitute for the information. Health professionals in training must look at the dead body, carefully and completely.

The principle is a respect for the body. Respect for dead bodies is traditional in all cultures, regardless of burial customs. Whether we bury the body whole, or embalm it, or cremate it, mutilation is allowed only upon cultural agreement of an overriding purpose, such as the education of health professionals. This purpose overrides our mutilation taboo.

We approve of dissection, with some religious exceptions. Dissenting religious traditions might include Orthodox Judaism, Christian Science, and Eastern Orthodox. Most Christian denominations have no specific objections to dissection, perhaps because of the theological recognition that God's miraculous power to raise the dead does not depend on an intact organ structure. Many Americans agree with dissection, comprising a pluralistic coalition of religious people, empiricists, and philosophers: those who believe, such as Christians, that the body is the temple of the spirit; those who believe the body is all there is; and those who believe the body is merely the agent of the mind and will.

The Cadaver as Gift

The Uniform Anatomical Gift Act specifies the conditions under which a "gift" of a body may be given to a medical school. Individuals carry cards which certify that in case of death they have dedicated their body to medical research and education. A medical school's department of anatomy has the right to use bodies—numerous bodies; the average number of bodies donated to most medical schools each year numbers in the hundreds. These bodies are received at medical schools, embalmed for long-lasting preservation (not for short-run aesthetic appearance, as at funeral homes), and readied for anatomical study.

We—and I speak now as a clinician and a citizen, for my days of dissection are long over—we approve of medical students, dentists, nurses, and allied health professionals using these bodies. We give students the gifts of these bodies. And what do we expect from them in return? Two things: grateful use and proper conduct. It would be wrong to treat something so important to the donor in an undignified manner, as merely a commodity. It would also be wrong to use or to handle such a gift as a body in a way the donor would condemn. No body parts should be passed from table to table, or thrown around, or taken from the lab. Those who have left their bodies for education have the right to see their most personal of gifts treated properly by students. They donate their bodies, giving them to students to whom they come both by chance and by choice for anatomic instruction.

Cadaver Funeral Service

My local chapter of the Christian Medical & Dental Society has been active in planning and conducting memorial services for the cadavers used in the anatomy lab. This is both an effective ministry and a witness. The ceremony is held in early December after the remains of the cadavers have been cremated. Family members are invited. In the few years we have had such a service, we have noticed that about half of the first-year class attends, many of the anatomy faculty attend, and often the dean is present. While in our experience only a few family members will be present, others who do not attend write and say they appreciate the thought of the ceremony.

The interdenominational service is short—twenty minutes or so—and begins with music and a greeting. Students express appreciation for the gifts of the bodies and sometimes read poems, light candles representing each donor, or say prayers. The main speaker is allowed no more than five minutes. Coffee and refreshments follow.

Conclusion

How shall students overcome their fear of the dead body, this most amazing gift? How shall they overcome the most primitive level of response to a corpse: their desire to flee? How then shall they face that which, if they think about it even for a few moments, will force them to consider both human dignity and human abjection? Both the freedom of thought and the limitations of the flesh?

Students will soon be at hard work, cutting and dissecting, looking at parts of the whole. Perhaps then they will wonder what the fuss was about, since they quickly overcame their initial awe of the remains of another human being. They will think about the organs in relation to each other and in terms of their structure and function. They will not have to face the whole cadaver again. They will soon have a dismantled tube of flesh.

But if we are to retain our Christian humanity, we must also remember that these bodies once were of a piece, once were alive, once hoped, dreamed, and loved. They were once even as we are now. They were fellow human beings who entrusted student doctors with their last remains, and they knew what the students are going to do to them. They ex-pected nothing less than complete dissection, for they ex-pected that students will learn from them what they can never learn from any other human being. They only chose to allow it—we in society will only allow it—because soon enough we will trust students with our living bodies. That is why cadaver ethics are important.

Part Four

Overcoming the World

13

The Call to Serve

B ecoming a member of a learned profession requires intensive study; the knowledge acquired sets the members
apart from those who, lacking such knowledge, depend on
the statements and acts of the professional. Medical histo-
rian Lester King writes: "Members of a profession thus
found themselves in a position of authority that rested on
trust. This dual relationship imposed on the members of a
profession a particular moral obligation, made explicit by
a code of ethics."[1]

A large amount of literature exists on the meaning of
profession. Most authors agree on five major elements of
a profession(al):

1. Service orientation
2. Specialized training and skills
3. Reasonable payment or salary
4. Formation of professional associations
5. Code of ethics

Many of these elements are now common among occupations formerly termed trades. In our service economy, many individuals possess specialized training and skills. Professional associations and codes of ethics are nearly ubiquitous. Business, as King points out, is undoubtedly in some of its aspects a profession today. When the Harvard Business School was founded, the president of Harvard University identified business as the newest of professions. But the clergy, health professionals, and lawyers are basically still regarded as the foremost among professionals.

Unfortunately, many health professionals find themselves losing control over their work and unable to set their own fees. To the extent that health professionals are learned and ethical enough to control their own work, obtain reasonable salaries, and agree on their own moral standards, they are professionals. To the extent that health professionals *lose* the power to control their own work, obtain payments, and promulgate their own codes of ethics, they become deprofessionalized.

The Process of Deprofessionalization

Deprofessionalization proceeds in the opposite direction of professionalization: the loss of control, the watering down of ethical codes, the weakening of licensure processes and professional associations, and the lowering of scholastic and quality control standards.

Clifton Dummett provides us with a picture of the process in the late 1800s: "Patients were not protected from practitioners with unscrupulous tendencies. It was difficult, often impossible, to ascertain whether some dentists were either capable or qualified to perform the services they advertised in an obtrusive fashion. The combination of privately owned schools, unregulated scholastic standards, implausible state licensing procedures, clamorous advertising, and proprietary journals all seemed to encourage the dissemination of im-

proper or even harmful services to the American people . . .
the [current] trend toward commercialization of the health
professions merits extensive analysis . . . undue emphasis on
business and profit-making aspects of health care can erode
the moral and ethical commitments of all health professionals to the welfare and the interests of the sick and disabled."[2]

Kramer has traced the effects of commercialization on the
changing language of ethical codes. He points out that one
of the distinguishing features of a profession has been the
requirement for its members "to adhere to principles of conduct loftier and more stringent than those governing com-
mercial enterprise."[3] Just as importantly, professionals are
called to serve others.

We serve the Lord by serving the patient. We are called
to be caregivers and healers: It is a vocation. Pellegrino puts
it this way:

> To be a physician is to be committed to a noble ideal. To be
> a Christian physician is to add dimensions of inspiration and
> aspiration that elevate the ideal immeasurably. The Chris-
> tian physician is called to imitate an ineffable model, an in-
> carnate God whose own ministry was inseparable from heal-
> ing. . . . Christian physicians have in Christ a more explicit
> model to inspire them than any profession other than the
> clergy. Healing was Jesus' daily task. He healed body and
> soul; in Him healing and salvation were one. Healing ex-
> emplified His love for men and women in the most concrete
> way. The Greek word *sozein* meant both to heal and to save.
> Christ had compassion on the vulnerability of the sick. He
> knew the meaning of bodily suffering, and Himself tasted it
> to the fullest in the garden of Gethsemane and on the cross.

Pellegrino continues, in pointing out the ministry of the
health professions:

> If they are to follow Christ, healing for Christian physicians
> cannot ever be anything other than ministry. It cannot ever

be merely science or even public service. Physicians heal insofar as medical knowledge allows. But they must also care for and feel for the sick, whether medical means are adequate or not. Christian compassion means to "suffer with" those who suffer. The Christian ministry of healing is not reserved for those who can pay, or for the educated, the grateful, the clean, for "our kind of people," or for those who "help themselves." It must be extended to all who suffer; it must be given with love to all, or it is not Christian. Christian physicians are authentic only if they unite their Christianity inseparably with their healing.[4]

Hal Habecker writes:

Work is a deeply spiritual experience. As a holy and royal priesthood, the work of all Christians is holy work [1 Peter 2:5, 9]. We are called not to a career but to a life of service for Christ Jesus. . . . Christian doctors ought to be the very first persons who call their professions to the moral foundations proclaimed in Scripture.[5]

The call gives us a service orientation; the need to be competent requires us to learn new skills.

Specialized Training and Skills

Health professionals also share common goals in treating patients. In the encounter between patient and clinician many appropriate goals are pursued simultaneously. These goals include the following:

1. restoration of health
2. prevention of disease
3. the relief of symptoms (including physical distress and psychological suffering)
4. the restoration of function or the maintenance of compromised function

5. the education and counseling of patients regarding their condition and its prognosis
6. the saving or prolonging of life
7. avoiding harm to the patient in the course of care[6]

In general, patients and caregivers both regard the ideal endpoint of a clinical encounter to be the identification and successful treatment of an entirely curable condition. Some believe the prevention of disease is an even greater benefit to both patient and clinician.

Essential to sound clinical judgment is a realistic understanding of the goals of treatment. In a clinical case, ethical deliberation should begin with a clear and realistic evaluation of the goals of the treatment. Which goals are desired should be determined jointly by patient and health professional after the patient has been informed by the caregiver which goals are possible.

In defining the goals, the health professional will consider the following:

1. The nature of the disease. What goals are achievable for this particular patient with this specific condition? What trade-offs must be made among the possible goals, for example, between relief of suffering and maximal preservation of function? Of course, any such determination must be expressed in probabilities rather than certainties.

2. The preferences of the patient. What are the patient's goals in this encounter? In many instances, the patient's goals are the same as the clinician's. It must be acknowledged, however, that for personal, psychological, social, religious, or economic reasons, the patient's goals may differ from those of the clinician.

3. Social, cultural, political, and economic realities. Any goals sought by clinicians and patients are pursued within a context of religious, social, cultural, political, and economic realities. Access to scarce resources, the wealth or poverty of individuals and communities, and religious and

cultural beliefs will facilitate the attainment of some goals and render others impossible.

When specialized training and skills are acquired, professionals can expect reasonable payment and often form associations which promulgate ethical codes. The Christian Medical & Dental Society provides an excellent example of the type of professional societies we need to join. CMDS cares about the spiritual needs of doctors, including the priority of Scripture, prayer, accountability, and kingdom seeking. It emphasizes the priority of sharing the good news, helps us recognize our vocation, calls us to be salt and light, and reminds us that Christian doctors care for the poor in America and overseas. Our active support of groups which represent us and our professional interests is critical. We need to pray for them, be involved in them personally, and support them.

One task of professional associations is the promulgation of ethical standards. CMDS has provided us with clinically relevant Christian codes of medical and dental ethics, which are printed below. These codes can help, because it is easy to lose sight of the relationship between excellent clinical practice and clinical ethics.

Biblical Model for Medical and Dental Ethics

Christians believe in the divine inspiration, integrity, and final authority of the Bible as the Word of God. This is our starting point for Christian medical and dental ethics. In affirming the authority of Scripture, we follow the command and example of the Lord Jesus Christ in whom all authority in heaven and earth is vested.

We believe that in His Word God has graciously provided us with the principles necessary to make difficult ethical decisions. Ethical concepts which are not specifically taught in Scripture can be derived from principles which are found there.

In addition, our ethical perspectives are guided by the Holy Spirit and by the teachings of Christian tradition, moral reasoning, and clinical experience. The circumstances of each case must be considered to discover the moral issues raised, but we do not accept such philosophies as ethical relativism, situational ethics, or utilitarianism. (Neither do we follow mindless legalism. Our Lord stated that the weightier matters of the law are justice, mercy, and faith in God.)

Biblical ethics is concerned with motives as well as actions, with process as well as outcome. The integrity of moral decisions rests on the prudent use of biblical principles. We acknowledge, however, that sincere Christians may differ in their interpretation and application of these principles.

Patients or their advocates, families, and clinicians are morally responsible for their own actions. We, as physicians and dentists, are ultimately responsible to God as we care for the health of our fellow human beings.

The Christian Physician's Oath

With gratitude to God, faith in Christ Jesus, and dependence on the Holy Spirit, I publicly profess my intent to practice medicine for the glory of God.

With humility, I will seek to increase my skills. I will respect those who teach me and who broaden my knowledge. In turn, I will freely impart my knowledge and wisdom to others.

With God's help, I will love those who come to me for healing and comfort. I will honor and care for each patient as a person made in the image of God, putting aside selfish interests.

With God's guidance, I will endeavor to be a good steward of my skills and of society's resources. I will convey God's love in my relationships with family, friends, and community. I will aspire to reflect God's mercy in caring for the lonely, the poor, the suffering, and the dying.

With God's blessing, I will respect the sanctity of human life. I will care for all my patients, rejecting those interventions which either intentionally destroy or actively end the lives of the unborn, the infirm, and the terminally ill.

With God's grace, I will live according to this profession.

Principles of Christian Excellence in Dental and Medical Practice

As Christian caregivers in the dental and medical professions, we commit ourselves to the following principles:

We will do no harm to our patients by acts of either omission or commission.

We are dedicated to the prevention and relief of human pain and suffering.

We hold all human life to be sacred as created in God's image.

We respect the confidentiality of all communications exchanged with our patients.

We affirm the standard of honesty in all circumstances.

We believe that our patients have the right to be carefully taught about all aspects of their disease and treatment so that they may give consent that is properly informed.

We pursue excellence in dentistry and medicine through the advancement of research and education.

Because we follow the example of our Lord and Savior Jesus Christ who came to earth "not to be ministered unto, but to minister and to give his life . . . ," we are dedicated to the service of all persons regardless of the state of their economic resources or the nature of their illness. In circumstances where their care is beyond our own resources, we will intervene on their behalf as advocates of adequate care.

We desire to maintain a quality of relationship with our patients which will bespeak our availability for counsel as well as care.

The Christian Dentist's Oath

With gratitude to God, faith in Christ Jesus, and dependence on the Holy Spirit, I publicly profess my intent to practice dentistry for the glory of God.

With humility, I will seek to increase my skills. I will respect those who teach me and who broaden my knowledge. In turn, I will freely impart my knowledge and wisdom to others.

With God's help, I will love those who come to me for healing and comfort. I will honor and care for each patient as a person made in the image of God, putting aside selfish interests.

With God's guidance, I will endeavor to be a good steward of my skills and of society's resources. I will convey God's love in my relationships with family, friends, and community. I will aspire to reflect God's mercy in caring for the lonely, the poor, the suffering, and the dying.

With God's blessing, I will respect the sanctity of human life. I will care for all my patients, rejecting those interventions which either intentionally destroy or actively end the lives of the unborn, the infirm, and the terminally ill.

With God's grace, I will live according to this profession.

Conclusion

The basics of the Christian health professions are ministry and service orientation, specialized training and skills, reasonable payment, membership in professional associations, and promulgation of codes of ethics. Deprofessionalization and greed lead us in the opposite direction. CMDS is an example of a professional organization which holds high professional ideals, including those of vocation, service, and ethics.

The public profession of our calling and desire to be doctors is a worthy action. We are not being idealistic or unrealistic when we say, "With gratitude to God, faith in Christ Jesus, and dependence on the Holy Spirit, I publicly profess my intent to practice medicine or dentistry for the glory of God." We are not being foolish when we say we will practice our profession, "With humility . . . with God's help . . . with God's guidance . . . with God's blessing . . . "

The reality is that we need God's help to be professional. May God grant us each the grace to live according to our calling and profession.

14

A Special Love for Gold

A woman was there who had been subject to bleeding for twelve years. She had suffered a great deal under the care of many doctors and had spent all she had, yet instead of getting better she grew worse. When she heard about Jesus, she came up behind him in the crowd and touched his cloak, because she thought, "If I just touch his clothes, I will be healed." Immediately her bleeding stopped and she felt in her body that she was freed from her suffering. At once Jesus realized that power had gone out from him. He turned around in the crowd and asked, "Who touched my clothes?" "You see the people crowding against you," his disciples answered, "and yet you can ask, 'Who touched me?'"

But Jesus kept looking around to see who had done it. Then the woman, knowing what had happened to her, came and fell at his feet and, trembling with fear, told him the whole truth. He said to her, "Daughter, your faith has healed you. Go in peace and be freed from your suffering."

—Mark 5:25–34

[Doctors have] a special love for gold.
—Chaucer, Canterbury Tales

The doctor was closing his bag now. He said, "When do you think you can pay this bill?" He said it even kindly.

137

> *"When I have sold my pearl I will pay you,"* Kino said.
> *"You have a pearl? A good pearl?"* the doctor asked with
> *interest.*
>
> —John Steinbeck, The Pearl

Medicine is changing, but rather than succumb to pessimism, we Christian healers can use this time of turmoil to be light and salt and to challenge those in our profession who have "a special love for gold." American physicians are increasingly concerned and disgruntled about the economics of medical practice. Major changes are occurring. Consider, for example, proposals for health care reform.

Potential plans for health care reform include an overall structure to contain costs and ensure access, a core benefit package, universal health benefits coverage, health networks, insurance reform, special provisions for small employers, medical malpractice reform, and slowed price increases on prescription drugs.

Reforms would establish a National Health Board made up of health care professionals and others to develop a core benefits package, as well as global budgets. Practice guidelines would be developed. Claims forms would be standardized. Drug prices would be cut. These are practical features of cost containment which have already been piloted and implemented in managed care. While the current controversy about our fees is sometimes uncomfortable, it is not unprecedented. One of the historical ethical dilemmas in medicine is the tension between altruism and greed. A review confirms that public scrutiny of physicians' wages has been ongoing and is not new.

Jesus as Healer

Jesus received no payment for his healings. As the passage in Mark 5 illustrates, other physicians of the time charged much for their services: The patient had "spent all she had." During his first reported evening clinic in the Gospel of Mark, we are told "the people brought to Jesus all the sick and demon-possessed. The whole town gathered at the door, and Jesus healed many who had various diseases" (Mark 1:32–34). "A man with leprosy came to him and begged, 'If you are willing, you can make me clean.' Filled with compassion, Jesus reached out his hand and touched the man. 'I am willing,' he said. 'Be clean!' Immediately the leprosy left the man and he was cured" (Mark 1:40–42).

A few days later, when Jesus entered Capernaum, some men came to him, four of them carrying a paralytic. "Since they could not get him to Jesus because of the crowd, they made an opening in the roof above Jesus and, after digging through it, lowered the mat the paralyzed man was lying on. When Jesus saw their faith, he said to the paralytic, 'Son, your sins are forgiven . . . I tell you, get up, take your mat and go home.' He got up, took his mat, and walked out in full view of them all. This amazed everyone and they praised God, saying, 'We have never seen anything like this!'" (Mark 2:1–12). Luke's accounts are similar. After the healing of the paralytic, the people "were filled with awe and said, 'We have seen remarkable things today'" (Luke 5:26).

Jesus, we know, "took up our infirmities and carried our sorrows, yet we considered him stricken by God, smitten by him, and afflicted" (Isa. 53:4). The dynamic of his healing ministry is outlined in the next verse in Isaiah: "But he was pierced for our transgressions, he was crushed for our iniquities; the punishment that brought us peace was upon him, and by his wounds we are healed" (v. 5).

These passages and numerous other accounts of Jesus' healing emphasize again and again that he came at personal cost. He had palpable and tangible healing power which he used for the benefit of the sick and the demon possessed, free of charge. He didn't need any classes on bedside manner; he was often moved by compassion or grief. His clinics were burgeoning.

The story of the woman who spent all she had on other physicians but was freely healed by Jesus emphasizes the charitable nature of Jesus' healing ministry as opposed to the usual, customary, and reasonable charges of the time. Besides implying the finances of Jesus' medical practice, the Bible's accounts of the rich fool, the rich man and Lazarus, and the rich young ruler emphasize his point: Life does not consist in the abundance of possessions but in richness toward God.

Jesus may have received contributions from his followers, and he shared meals with them, but he was not troubled or anxious about money. These are his words to worried, covetous, greedy, gluttonous disciples like us:

> Therefore I tell you, do not worry about your life, what you will eat; or about your body, what you will wear. Life is more than food, and the body more than clothes. Consider the ravens: They do not sow or reap, they have no storeroom or barn; yet God feeds them. And how much more valuable you are than birds! Who of you by worrying can add a single hour to his life? Since you cannot do this very little thing, why do you worry about the rest?
>
> Consider how the lilies grow. They do not labor or spin. Yet I tell you, not even Solomon in all his splendor was dressed like one of these. If that is how God clothes the grass of the field, which is here today, and tomorrow is thrown into the fire, how much more will he clothe you, O you of little faith! And do not set your heart on what you will eat or drink; do not worry about it. For the pagan world runs after all such things, and your Father knows that you need them. But seek his kingdom, and these things will be given to you as well.
>
> Do not be afraid, little flock, for your Father has been pleased to give you the kingdom. Sell your possessions and give to the poor. Provide purses for yourselves that will not

wear out, a treasure in heaven that will not be exhausted, where no thief comes near and no moth destroys. For where your treasure is, there your heart will be also (Luke 12:22–34).

Jesus healed freely and instructed his disciples to do likewise: "Heal the sick, raise the dead, cleanse those who have leprosy, drive out demons. Freely you have received, freely give" (Matt. 10:8). He told us that the conflict between our love for God and our love for money is one of the most fundamental ethical tensions in our lives.

Physicians have been insulated from this tension for the last several decades by the creation of third-party payers and the development of a remarkably generous medical system. Even those of us with a "special love of gold" have been happy. Current cost constraint measures and proposals for government intervention, however, force us to reconsider our motivations for practicing medicine. A historic review can help us better understand our modern dilemma.

From Trephination to House Calls: A Historical Perspective on Physicians' Salaries

Skull trephination is one of the first known medical procedures. A hole was chiseled through the skull, presumably for release of noxious humors or relief of headache. Prehistoric skulls show evidence of trephination and even of healing at the site, so some of the patients survived the procedure. Nonetheless, for procedures with this degree of risk, I assume, payment was at the time of service. Early on, the profession of medicine struggled with the problem of fees. How could physicians consider themselves healers and at the same time earn a living? The Latin word for profession, *profiteor*, means "to make a public statement or announcement of a special skill." The word *profession* is closely linked to the Christian concept of "vocation" or "calling," but the word *profit* is visible in the root word as well. Aristophanes and Sophocles debated whether medicine was a trade or a profession; Aristophanes contended that medicine was an art, but Sophocles asserted that the physician was merely a hired hand, a tradesman. The debate continues today. Socrates noted that money was important. "Unless pay is added to the art," he wrote, "there would be no benefit for the craftsman, and consequently he would be unwilling to go to the trouble of taking care of the trouble of others."[1]

The physician Galen was more cautious: "It is not possible to pursue the true goal of medicine if one holds wealth more important than virtue, and learns this art not to help people, but for material gain."[2]

Hippocrates, a wealthy physician of noble birth who eschewed fees, noted that since physicians save people from death, "no fee, not even a large one, is adequate for the physician, but it is with God Almighty that his remuneration rests—and what he may receive should be reckoned as a gift, a present." Hippocrates, however, also realized that some doctors needed to charge a fee, and he said in his Precepts that the doctor should be kindhearted and willing to accommodate his fee to the patient's circumstance.[3]

Over the last two millennia, physicians have struggled with the issue of remuneration. Ibn al-Tilmidh, a Christian physician in Baghdad, would not accept any gift unless the patient were a caliph or sultan. In Renaissance Venice, physicians and surgeons enjoyed modest to high incomes; the largest recorded salary per year, thirteen lire di grossi, was received by surgeon Master Gualtieri, an apparent victim of the plague in 1348.

An Irish physician, Thomas Arthur (1593–1674), wrote in his diary in 1619: "The amount of my fees for this year is 74 pounds 8 shillings, for which and for other gifts conferred upon me, unworthy, I return boundless thanks to the Almighty God, Who has thus deigned to bless the beginning of my medical practice; and I beg of him to vouchsafe, to direct, govern, and sanctify the rest of my actions, to the praise and glory of His Name, through Christ our Lord, Amen."[4]

Among Arthur's first entries for 1620 are:

"I went to Dublin to Mr. George Sexton (Gonorrhoea laborantem), who being thoroughly cured, gave me a horse of the value of 13 pounds gold. I then went to the lady of Arthur Chicester . . . the treasurer of this kingdom . . . in Ulster . . . labouring under dropsy . . . and forewarning her of her death within a few days after my prognosis, I attended upon [her]; I received 15 pounds. I went to Margaret Walsh, the daughter of Cormac O'Hara, who was pregnant, and became convalescent without injury to herself or the child— 1 pound; Sir Randel M'Saurley . . . sent for me to Dunluce, and gave me 1 pound."

Dr. Isaac Senter (1753–1799), a surgeon in Rhode Island, received $8 for a delivery, $20 for a thigh amputation, and $14 for inoculating a man and his wife for smallpox (which would necessitate daily house calls for a week while they recovered from their mild attacks). Senter paid $1 a day to a man to build a fence, and $1.50 a day to a man working on his house. He bought a live hog weighing 122 pounds for $5. A shirt cost $1.50. His son went to Rhode Island College (now Brown) for $100 per year.[5]

Lessons from the Past:
Professionalism and Professional Fees

A review of these and other historical documents reveals that for several hundred years British physicians made the equivalent of about 1 gold pound (or one guinea) per visit. The Oxford English dictionary still defines a guinea as the unit for a professional fee, and the coin continued to be the unit of consultation on Britain's fashionable Harley Street even after the decimalization of the coinage in 1971. Although it was expressed in dollar equivalents, the guinea was the standard fee in America as well. In Isaac Senter's time a guinea was worth about $4, so he charged the standard 2 guineas for a delivery. Dr. Arthur's usual house-call fee was 1 pound; he received more, however, from the grateful patient "cured" of gonorrhea, and from the wealthy husband of the woman with dropsy.

Several points are worth noting. First, a guinea (adjusting for inflation) is worth about $46.50 today. Thus, a patient visit should be worth about $50; office fees of modern physicians are not far from this figure, and because of increased overhead might even be comparably less than in the past. Of course surgical fees and delivery fees are much higher, reflecting the increased technology available in this area. How much money should physicians make? Historically, they should earn the equivalent of a gold guinea as their base office fee adjusted for overhead.

Second, historical data about physician income in numerous cultures reveals the interesting finding that physicians in general have earned about four times as much as day laborers, although the ratio varies between two- and ten-fold.

Third, the debate over physicians' incomes is an old one; the modern controversy is just a resurgence in the ongoing controversy. An 1856 textbook noted, "Every impartial observer, in contemplating the rapid augmentation of the fees of physicians of the past thirty years, must be struck with astonishment at the magnitude of the imposition, and the oppressive amount of their extractions. If they [the doctors] go on thirty more years at the rate they have for the thirty past, the whole community will be little better than the slaves of the medical faculty. . . . We are far from wishing to see medical fees reduced down to the mere compensation of an ordinary day laborer—far from it. But we desire to see them so modified that it may not require the wages of a laborer for a quarter of a year to pay the physician for one day's [hospitalization]."[6]

Fourth, the personal choice between economic interest and altruism has also existed throughout history. Philosophers and physicians have addressed this issue in an attempt to balance the doctor's need to earn a living and the need of the poor for care.

Fifth, whatever their finances, Christian health professionals can give thanks. Dr. Thomas Arthur, an obscure Irish physician who was by no means wealthy, gives us an important historical example in giving abundant thanks to God for his meager fees. Arthur goes on, in his accounting statement of one of his first years in practice, to ask God to direct, control, and sanctify his actions.

The Challenge

What lies ahead for American physicians? According to Eli Ginzberg, a respected medical economist, the supply of physicians will continue to increase, and unless total spending for health care accelerates or physicians can redirect the flow of hospital funds to themselves, physician incomes will be reduced, probably appreciably. Hospitals will merge and close, and staff appointments will become more difficult to obtain. Due to competition from other modes of health care, visits to physicians will decline. Congress will continue to freeze physicians' fees and institute other means and reforms to eliminate the usual, customary, and reasonable fee determination. Recent medical school graduates will opt for corporate employment. "Even if some of the warnings prove to be unwarranted," Ginzberg writes, "the outlook for physicians has definitely taken a marked turn for the worse."[7]

We can view the words of medical futurists with alarm if we wish. We can retire. We can tell our children to avoid the health professions as careers, and we can grumble and complain about our salaries (although since we earn about four times as much as the average American, we can expect little sympathy). We can argue that our particular specialty should make more money than some other specialty (the old-fashioned word for this particular maneuver is *coveting*).

I am convinced that Christian health professionals can do better than this. We do need to discuss these issues together; we should be concerned about the clinical and personal impact of the current medical economic upheaval. We need to be sensitive to those physicians who experience financial difficulty.

But we also need to remember that despite doom and gloom predictions, there is historical evidence that physicians will continue to earn their guinea per visit and make two to ten times as much as the average worker. Adjustments in our lifestyles may be necessary, but we can encourage each other instead of discourage each other. We can even be thankful (remember Dr. Arthur's end-of-year audit) for what God has given us.

Our perspective on payment for healing enables us to work as unto the Lord. We cannot escape who we are—followers of him who healed for free. He taught us we cannot serve God and mammon. Even if physicians' salaries drop fairly dramatically, we have a model of medicine which transcends any economic models. What a critical time for Christian young people to be entering medicine! We need to stop discouraging them. God can use them, here or elsewhere in the world. Medicine needs them!

Some doctors have an interest in pearls and a special love for gold. The current state of medicine will make them unhappy, but we need to keep our eyes on the eternal prize. Jesus was talking to us when he said, "Do not be afraid, little flock, for your Father has been pleased to give you the kingdom."

15

Medical Economics and the Free-Lunch Syndrome

The morning's mail was typical: home health care orders, medical journals, insurance company forms, lab reports. But a handsome, gold-lettered envelope caught my eye. It was an invitation to a dinner at an extravagant downtown hotel.

If I attended this dinner the hostess promised to give me a check for $100. And to add a touch of tingle-tangle to the proposition, I knew her to be an extremely attractive, single young woman. She was inviting me—a tired and somewhat worn primary care doctor—to dine with her and listen to her pleasant and engaging conversation.

So What's the Catch?

A free meal, $100, an attractive hostess—so what's the catch, you ask? Good question, and one which many health professionals and their spouses fail to ask. The first catch is that I am a happily married man with a lovely wife who is

147

a wonderful dinner companion (and she was not invited). The second catch is that the hostess is a skilled pharmaceutical sales representative who will use the opportunity to promote her company's products to me and the other physicians present.

The third catch is that the $150 she would spend on each of us represents, in miniature, the global marketing strategy that the drug industry considers its best and most efficient advertising. Pharmaceutical advertising expenditures are estimated to amount to more than 25 percent of sales revenue.

More than one-third of the pharmaceutical industry's promotional budget is allotted to representative activities, and there is one rep for every fifteen physicians. Drug companies spend three billion dollars, or approximately five thousand dollars per United States physician, in this way each year. The pharmaceutical industry actually spends more on pharmaceutical sales representative activities than it does on the raw materials for its products.

And the fourth and final catch is, even if my wife were invited and if I accepted the invitation, my patients would eventually pay for the whole thing.

I call this the free-lunch syndrome: mild to moderate greed, mild and early compromise of ethical standards, all found in the clinical setting of pharmaceutical promotional activities. The free-lunch syndrome seems to afflict many otherwise ethical physicians and their families.

Doctors who wouldn't even think of overbilling, splitting fees, "buying" patients from referring physicians, or falsifying income tax returns seem to think drug company payola is just fine. The syndrome is found worldwide. In Great Britain a drug company overrode physicians' normally cautious attitudes toward new drugs by entertaining them at conferences held on the Orient Express enroute to Venice. Swedish physicians were given tickets to shows featuring nude dancers. Physicians in Canada were taken on fly-in fishing trips.

Reports of Controversial Pharmaceutical Promotional Activities

The following reports are not intended to make a general statement about the pharmaceutical industry nor to cause the reader to mistrust physicians or the medications they prescribe. They do illustrate the temptations the companies and doctors must guard against.

Biased and premature marketing of Opren, a British non-steroidal anti-inflammatory drug, featured dubious clinical data presented at conferences in attractive venues. Sixty deaths and many cases of photosensitivity dermatitis were attributed to Opren; the product was abruptly withdrawn from the market.[1]

One hundred dollars for dinner and an additional $100 if doctor brought a colleague to hear a talk on an intravenous globulin preparation.[2]

Bogus clinical trials (brief, uncontrolled, scientifically useless studies not approved by IRBs.) Studies done in doctors' offices on five to ten patients who pay for both medical care and drugs; physicians are given a sum for each patient.[3]

Frequent flyer program for physicians who prescribe Inderal Long Acting; free coach ticket if they prescribe the drug for fifty patients and fill out a seven-question survey; escalating prizes for more patients up to a maximum of two hundred.[4]

"Educational Conference." An invited speaker reported that he was to receive $1500 to speak at a conference sponsored by a drug company; he declined when he discovered that all one hundred conference attendees were physicians whose expenses (travel with spouses, hotel rooms, open bar at a reception, and meals) were to be completely covered by the pharmaceutical company for a few days. Each physician was invited by his local rep to attend this "symposium" which was to consist of only two morning's lectures.[5]

Feldene sun shields, which provide direct advertising to the public when placed on physicians' dashboards. Unlike most sun shields, the flip side contains more drug information instead of the usual and beneficial message on sun shields, "Send Help!"[6]

Methods of Drug Promotion

Methods of drug promotion are as varied as the companies and the physicians they target. Expensive junkets, golf and tennis outings, weekend getaways, fancy meals, frequent flyer tickets—these are the more ostentatious offerings reported in the medical literature. Then there are the modest forms of promotion: Post-it notes, pens, cups, flashlights, etc., all emblazoned with the company logo. Most medical students are given their first stethoscopes and EKG calipers by drug companies.

Other promotional gifts are less conspicuous, even charitable: free medications for poor patients, donations to medical student groups, textbooks for house officers (residents).

Physician acceptance of promotional gifts may be illegal in certain settings. For instance, acceptance of money or other gratuities by Veteran's Administration physicians can represent a conflict of interest and breach of contract. Thirty-two VA employees were disciplined for their involvement with five pharmaceutical companies, which included attending or speaking at meetings sponsored by the companies.

More commonly, however, the free-lunch syndrome is a clinical and ethical problem, not a legal one. What are the implications of drug company gift giving? Where should we draw the line? What are the ethical principles which can guide Christian physicians as we consider our interactions with pharmaceutical companies and sales representatives?

Gift-Giving

First, gifts have strings. Whenever a physician accepts a gift from a drug company, an implicit relationship is established. A gift is a proffer of friendship; accepting a gift triggers an obligation and refusing a gift signals a rejection of the relationship. The more conscientious a person, the more likely he or she is to respond to these feelings and obligations. In other words, a gift is given to engender a response. I know personally that when I accept even a small gift from a salesperson (a pen or a coffee cup, for example) I feel constrained to at least listen to the presentation and look at the brochures.

Second, gifts cost money, and patients ultimately pay the bill. Acceptance of large gifts may contribute to the perception that physicians serve their own interests more than their patients' interests. But, as members of a profession we have the responsibility of regulating our own practices. Therefore, when we actively seek gifts, we lose our ethical moorings and become selfish.

Third, those of us who have experienced grace know that it is a supernatural and heavenly process; on our human level, gifts can bring complexities, stresses, and dangers. Consider that gifts can make even Christmas into a miserable time of the year. My father, a highly ethical man who recently retired from the pulp and paper business, was shocked when he first heard how naive physicians are about the power of gifts and of gift-giving practices. "How could you just accept a gift from a supplier?" he asked me. "I wouldn't allow any of my people to take even a small personal gift. Not one package of cheese. If one of our wood suppliers wanted to take one of us out for lunch, my policy was, "No, we'll go on our own or we'll take turns paying!"

Ethical Principles

Repeatedly we are told in the Scriptures that care for the poor and the disenfranchised is a moral good and a Christian imperative. What justification is there, then, for going out to lunches paid for with money which ultimately comes from our patients, many of whom are in difficult financial straits? Would you want your poorest patients to be asked to subsidize your family's drug company-sponsored trip to the Bahamas? How does this action differ from "imposing heavy rent on the poor" which the prophet Amos warned against? Indeed, God has told us what is good and what he requires, which is to do justice, to love kindness, and to walk humbly with him.

These crucial concepts—worship, altruism, and justice—can help us as we construct our professional and personal guidelines regarding physician-pharmaceutical company interactions. Here are my own recommendations:

General Principles

1. The physician serves the patient and should act in the patient's best interests.
2. The reality is that the patient actually pays for promotional activities in increased medication prices.
3. A gift which could compromise the physician's clinical objectivity should be refused.
4. A gift which would embarrass the physician if it were generally known should be refused.
5. A lavish gift ($100 or more) should be refused.

Specific Guidelines

1. *Clearly acceptable:*
   reprints of scientific articles
   free medications for poor patients

2. *Probably acceptable:*
   pens
   calendars
   coffee mugs
   flashlights
   other assorted minor knickknacks
   legitimate displays and teaching exercises
   printing of abstract booklets
   travel awards, based on need, for residents
   research support for legitimate trials of new drugs
   modest refreshment at a conference (e.g., pizza for the ward team)
   receptions related to educational purpose
   trips to sites chosen for convenience, not scenery
   standard honoraria for lecture
   stethoscopes and other ordinary medical instruments
   textbooks

3. *Probably not acceptable:*
   free travel for practicing physicians
   trips to sites chosen for scenery, not convenience
   tickets for celebrity performances or sporting events
   visible display of drug company paraphernalia (e.g., Feldene sun shield)
   meals at fine restaurants
   computers
   expensive medical instruments (e.g., endoscopes)

4. *Clearly unacceptable:*
   lavish refreshments
   exotic trips
   bogus clinical trials
   frequent flyer tickets
   accepting research support tied to "a good word with
   the formulary committee"

The Food and Drug Administration's regulation of pharmaceutical advertising defines "education" as scientific exchange and considers activities more promotional than educational when long-term or ongoing financial relationships exist between the speakers and the company.[7] Physical location and ambience are also factors in determining whether symposia are promotional or educational. These distinctions, admittedly, are subjective.

Some consensus exists, however. In a recent study, my colleagues and I found that more than half of the physicians we surveyed thought that acceptance of gifts worth more than $100 could compromise a physician's independence and objectivity.[8] I like to use the $100 cutoff in advising physicians and policymakers about the free-lunch syndrome.

As in many areas of medicine, a Spirit-guided conscience is the Christian doctor's bottom line. Some may be able to accept larger gifts without being vulnerable to a dependency relationship with a pharmaceutical company. Some may be at risk even at a lower figure. Motive and intention are always as important (or more important) than the actual dollar figure. Also, as the British guidelines point out, we can ask ourselves, "Would we be willing to have these arrangements generally known?"

As Christian physicians, we need to be aware of the injustice of the free-lunch syndrome. We need to set an example of ethical behavior which rejects payola. We can and should continue talking with pharmaceutical sales representatives; they convey valuable information about their products. But we should not accept gifts which, as the Royal College of Physicians puts it, might "influence the objectivity of prescribing behavior."[9] The American College of Physicians notes that accepting small gifts (pens, calendars) or modest hospitality clearly related to education is acceptable.[10]

Search your heart, pray about it, talk with your family and your colleagues, and draw your own personal line—and then stick to your standards.

Conclusion

Some final closing notes. In my time as a member of the Christian Medical & Dental Society and the CMDS Ethics Commission, I've talked with many physicians about medical ethics issues. One of the most thoughtful and courageous Christian physicians I know is employed full time by the pharmaceutical industry. Several people who are representatives attend our church and are active in Christian service. Most drug salespeople are highly ethical, and most of the products they promote are safe and highly efficacious.

The free-lunch syndrome is not a disease the pharmaceutical companies created. They are in business to sell their products, and they have found that a free lunch is the best, and sometimes the only, way to turn a doctor's head and get his or her full attention. But the companies only provide the setting for the free-lunch syndrome. The greed and ethical compromise which actually cause the syndrome come from within our own physician hearts.

So what's the cure for the syndrome? We can recognize the symptoms and begin effective treatment with repentance and change. We can "just say no" to drug company dinners, and we can say yes to representatives when they just ask to talk. We should want to talk about medications which can help our patients. As patients and caregivers we want to trust our doctors, their studies, and medications, but we should also carefully read the investigative protocols of experiments. We need to be informed to some degree about medicines and experiments. As health professionals it's time for personal action. Let's stop accepting payola. We know there's no such thing as a free lunch. Let's do better than Esau, who sold what was his for a bowl of good soup. We have knowledge which can help our patients; we have skills and training which enable us to act in their best interests. We should refuse any gift which would distract us from this role or jeopardize our professional integrity.

16

Medical Economics and the Chief's Wife

The chief's wife had an ovarian cyst. Either that or she was nine months pregnant, but since she was nearly sixty, that seemed unlikely.

The cyst was a big one; when we examined her we estimated it would weigh over fifty pounds, fluid and all. She needed surgery. Would she travel to our hospital soon to have surgery?

"She is the chief's wife," the interpreter told us.

"We need to operate on the cyst to remove it," we said.

"Of course," the interpreter said. "But she is the chief's wife. She will need to pay."

"We are missionary doctors," we said. "We do not need her money. Others have already paid for us to come here. We can operate on her for free. If she wishes to give $5.00 a day to cover her hospital room fee, it would be most generous of her."

"She says she will pay for the surgery, as much as a chief's wife would pay," said the interpreter, while the woman nodded and waited for our reply. Her abdomen was taut; she had great difficulty walking. The cyst was probably not cancer; still, we would have to remove it carefully to avoid spilling its contents inside her abdomen. The surgeon had done many such surgeries.

"Fifty or $75 would be great plenty, thank you," we told the interpreter.

A lengthy discussion ensued, involving the chief, the chief's wife, and our interpreter.

"She thinks she is worth more. She has heard that in America such surgery is very expensive. She is as good as American woman."

"It is true, we say, she is an old ma and greatly to be honored. She has many children. She is the chief's wife. How much will she pay for the surgery?"

"She says the surgery should cost at least $175," the interpreter told us.

"Tell the old ma she is right," we said. "She must bring the money when she comes, in cash. We will do the surgery for her then."

Weeks passed. We knew that even a chief, often the wealthiest man in the village, was unlikely to make much more than $30.00 per month. He would be selling livestock, trading goods, possibly even asking wealthy relatives for contributions.

One day the entourage arrived. The chief brought the money—dirty, carefully folded American five-dollar bills, thirty-five of them. The hospital treasurer put them in a little metal box, and the procession entered the hospital with great dignity.

The operation went well. Without the massive cyst, the woman's abdomen was hollow, scaphoid. We delivered her of the cyst and then withdrew its fluid, an amber blood-wine substance which flowed into bottle after bottle.

She did well postoperatively, did not have any infection, and the wound was healing well. Soon it was time for her to leave. We wondered how she felt without her massive, protuberant belly. She was finally able to walk about freely.

"The old ma can go as soon as she feels well," we said.

"The doctors have helped me," she said through the interpreter. "Tell them they have done well. Their work is good. They deserve to be paid much money for such work."

"We do not do it for the money, old ma," said the surgeon. "We do it because we want to help you. We stay out of the money business here. This is God's business."

"But you must never work for free," said the chief's wife. "Then the person is worth nothing. Each person will pay you what they are worth, and what the doctor's work is worth. It must be so. I have been here many years, and I know this how the people live."

"Thank you, old ma," we said. "You have many children. You are the chief's wife. May you have many grandchildren who live."

"I will go soon," she said.

The next day the group left. We never found out how they gathered the money. We never knew how they had selected the exact day to come for surgery. But the chief's wife taught us a lesson in medical economics. The doctor's teacher is the patient, who can help us set the price. It will not be too low, not even in the two-thirds world. It will reflect the patient's situation and the nature of the doctor's work. The price will be nearly nothing for some and many dollars for others.

But in Africa, when you operate on an ovarian cyst in an old ma who is the chief's wife, you must take money from her for the procedure. Then she will feel so happy about her treatment. Then she will walk into her village like a chief's wife, thin and strong, swaying slightly side-to-side like a young girl again.

17

Letters from the Twenty-first Century

My Dear Timothy:

You can't know how happy I am that you have finally chosen to practice medicine. I am glad you gave up that notion of becoming a spokesmodel for ArtifBody. With your medical background and interest in people, you belong in the clinic. You will find medicine a good and helpful profession, obviously not perfect. (There's still far too much selfishness in it for my liking, but the plague has helped some with this problem.) Remember, healing was one of the master's priorities, and while practically everything else has changed, he has not. Doctors can touch body and soul! So I happen to think medicine is an art worth spending your life on. Look at me; I am living proof that doctors *can* age. And being the old and pompous duff that I am, when I heard about your decision to be a plague doctor, I decided to write to you immediately.

In these few letters I'll try to tell you how it was for me back in the 1980s and 1990s, when the plague first struck. I was young in those days, and I remember it all as if it were yesterday. Pay attention now, or I'll personally see to it that the med committee makes you take the compuboards twice for good measure. Save these letters on one of those fancy SuperConductoDiscs of yours!

I do remember the plague well, but I'm too tired to write much more now. I am doing this by hand since I hate these newfangled TalkaWrites. (I know, you bought me one for Christmas. Sorry. I am too old, cranky, and truthful to lie about it.) They seem to force me to use my left brain much more than I like. Remember, Timothy, the right brain is often on to something. I just can't remember what.

2 Thessalonians 3:16–17,
Uncle Luke

My Dear Timothy:

We might as well start with the facts. I hope you'll be impressed with this proof of my memory. It was more than thirty years ago, but it was such a terrible time that the numbers are etched upon my mind.

As of early 1991, about 270,000 cases of AIDS were reported in the United States, and by 1994 more than 350,000 active cases had been reported. In San Francisco, which had 20,000 cases by 1993, the number of deaths from AIDS by the end of the '90s exceeded the death toll in that city from all the wars of the twentieth century.

By 1994, it was estimated that as many as two million Americans were infected with the AIDS virus. In America, AIDS was reported in all age groups, including children and those over sixty-five. Over 70 percent of the cases had occurred in homosexual or bisexual men, 20 percent in intravenous drug abusers, 2 percent in people who received contaminated blood, 1 percent in hemophiliacs, and the remainder in heterosexuals or persons who died before complete histories could be obtained.

Timothy, you know how upset I get when you think only about America, so I won't make the same mistake. By 1994, AIDS was already a severe problem in central Africa, where it was clearly a heterosexual disease. About one in five persons was infected (extreme poverty made it difficult to estimate the true prevalence). Our surgeon general in the late 1980s (I much prefer the term *surgeon general* to our modern *lasersurg general*), whose name was C. Everett Koop, was a Christian. He called for an international effort to deal with the worldwide problem of AIDS. Dr. Jonathan Mann, who was World Health Organization (WHO) coordinator for AIDS, warned that the epidemic would force the WHO to abandon much of its work on measles, malnutrition, and childhood diarrhea.

Of course, they were right. You don't have to know much history to recall what happened The average amount of money available per capita for health care in many of those countries would not even pay for a child's HIV antibody test, let alone drug therapy. By the start of the twenty-first century 100 million people had died of AIDS worldwide.

But I still remember very well the time—1993 or 1994 or so—when AIDS, like the bubonic plague of the Middle Ages, was declared a pandemic, a worldwide plague. That was when I realized I was a plague doctor.

What I'm telling you next may seem strange, and I know you think we were archaic, but we really had trouble treating those first patients. Although the treatment is quite good now, we still have the plague today. In those first days, we could do very little for AIDS patients. I'll tell you about it next time. In the meantime, study! And I don't mean the Clinitron! I mean study the Word also!

Hebrews 4:12–15,
Uncle Luke

My Dear Timothy:

My first AIDS patients were named, shall we say, Mr. Smith, Mr. Nelson, and Mr. Jones. I know these names seem simple to you, but I much prefer them to our confusing multiply hyphenated modern names: Mr. Smith-Nelson-Jones. It used to be that we all had belly buttons, knew who our parents were, and took our fathers' names. I will never get used to the artificial wombers' names (PL–35 should not be *anyone's* name). But a person is still a person by any name.

Anyway, I remember Smith, Nelson, and Jones. They developed parasitic pneumonias, fungal meningitis, widespread tuberculosis, disseminated herpes, and unusual cancers like Kaposi's sarcoma. They were gay men.

But as early as 1994 we could predict that AIDS would be a heterosexual disease in America, spreading especially in teenagers. Very few heterosexuals took us seriously, however. Remember, in Africa, the male-to-female ratio of the AIDS patients was already 1:1, and it took until 2015 for this to occur in the United States. By 1994 AIDS was slowly spreading into the heterosexual population, and the number of women with the disease was rapidly increasing. There was evidence that transmission could occur from a single sexual encounter. Contrary to earlier speculation, we found that the virus was transmitted from women to men and vice versa during vaginal intercourse. Since mother and child are in intimate contact, an increasingly common mode of transmission was from infected mothers to infants in utero, during birth, and through breast feeding. Women whose sex partners used IV drugs and shared needles were also at great risk.

Because AIDS has such a long incubation period, as you know, and it may be more than seven years from the time of infection until someone actually develops the symptoms, having sex was like having sex not only with the partner, but with every person with whom that partner has had sex. I used to tell my patients this example:

Sixteen-year-old Heather thinks she may have sex with sixteen-year-old Andy. It would be her first sexual experience. But what she doesn't know is that Andy has had sexual intercourse with Susan, who has previously had sex with William and Brian. Susan didn't know that Brian was an asymptomatic carrier of the AIDS virus. For that matter, neither did Brian.

So Heather is connected by a web of sexual contacts to someone who can transmit the AIDS virus. Whether or not she will get AIDS depends on how many in the group actually became infected by the virus. It is very unlikely that they would all have become infected, but it is possible. Thus, on her very first sexual contact, Heather actually has at least a small risk of exposure to the human immunodeficiency virus.

You know what my patients said? Some believed me and stopped having sex outside of marriage. Others thought I was an old duff even then. I was at the bedside of some of those when they died of AIDS. I loved them anyway.

While many of the individual diseases associated with AIDS could be treated even then, they often occurred in combination, and there was no curative treatment for the underlying disease itself. For example, Mr. Jones had two different kinds of viral pneumonia and three different types of parasitic and bacterial diarrhea. We had to use several antibiotics, and Mr. Jones developed multiple side effects.

You may not believe this, but we were able to cure several of these infections. Unfortunately, he still had no immune system of his own to protect him, and he went on to develop new infections. We needed a drug to treat the problem: AIDS itself.

There was only one really effective drug against AIDS in 1994; the antiviral drug Azidothymidine (AZT). Unfortunately, the increase in survival time was limited to several years, because AZT couldn't completely reverse the underlying immune system destruction caused by the virus. Drugs designed to boost the immune system were only in the early testing phase; we didn't have Immunogen yet.

As you know from your study of marrowkinetics, AZT was somewhat toxic (and I am embarrassed to say, quite expensive). Just for the record, I didn't go on any expensive trips sponsored by AZT companies. But somehow the medicine cost so much. Anyway a quarter of those treated developed anemia and some required ongoing transfusions. AZT had to be taken for the rest of the life of the AIDS patient.

The only way to stop the AIDS plague—and you must admit that it is still true today—was to prevent the transmission of the AIDS virus. Next time I'll tell you some of our thoughts about how to do this.

I hear from old Dr. Williams that you have been attending the Christian Medical & Dental Society meetings. Good. Don't forget all the things I have told you. Keep company with the master! Who can stand alone? Even I do not lean on my own understanding, I who have been a plague doctor these many, many long years.

Proverbs 3:1–12,
Uncle Luke

My Dear Timothy:

I know your research in cellular culture and subcellular biochemical communication has made you keenly aware of how different each cell is. When we first discovered AIDS, we realized that the human immunodeficiency virus (HIV) could infect and damage many types of cells, especially white blood cells of the immune system. HIV could (and can!) attack many tissues, including the vagina, cervix, male and female urethra, rectum, and brain. In the cells of these tissues, HIV is incorporated directly into the DNA (but you know all this).

Semen, vaginal fluid, and blood of infected persons contain large numbers of both infected white cells and viral particles. While the AIDS virus is present in most body fluids including saliva, the only methods of transmission which were major problems involved intimate sexual contact or contact with AIDS-contaminated blood. As you know, that remains pretty much the case today, with several notable exceptions which we couldn't completely foresee.

Through the early part of the epidemic we got no help from the media, who looked for quick fixes and kept producing their sex-without-consequences trash. I used to get so angry watching television! Even now, nearly a half-century later, I remember how I felt about those foolish ads pushing sex, the mindless and amoral sitcoms, the Solid Silver dancers. The media cost us thousands of lives, hundreds of thousands really, because they would not acknowledge the real consequences of promiscuous sexual behavior, sexually transmitted diseases, and pregnancy. But of course, the blame was ours as well. I always said I was too busy being a plague doctor to do anything about it. I never protested, never wrote a letter, never boycotted a sponsor. And to my shame I will tell you that after a day of watching people die, I sometimes liked watching the shows.

How wrong I was! How sinful to even acknowledge that message of sex! For I, of all people, knew that it was as if I was really visiting a prostitute, a whore who had covered over her secondary syphilis rash with "beauty spots." It was as if I myself were the whore. Underneath was corruption and death. Remember, Timothy. Remember, even for yourself. Have sense and repent.

Proverbs 7:6–27,
Uncle Luke

My Dear Timothy,

Besides sexual activity, we knew that AIDS could also be

transmitted through nonsexual means, usually involving the significant exchange of blood or bodily secretions. Even then, the bulk of evidence seemed to support our current understanding that household contacts, school contacts, and other casual human contacts do not result in the transmission of the virus.

AIDS was, however, easily transmitted nonsexually by practices common among certain intravenous drug abusers. I know this practice has virtually died out along with its adherents, but let me tell you how it was. These addicts not only shared needles; actually, when they "shot up," they drew relatively large quantities of blood up into the syringe. They did this to make sure they were injecting drug into a vein. The needle and the blood-coated syringe were then shared with another addict, and another; besides drugs, the syringe was eventually loaded with the AIDS virus and viral-infected white cells.

I know this needle business sounds barbaric, but think of the young people who use Braindust today, despite the dangers of engram loss. These were the kinds of people who took drugs intravenously. They cared so little about themselves, and their god was one of white dust instead of the gold dust the Israelites worshiped.

In New York, New Jersey, and Connecticut, and in big cities in the midwest and west, where there were many "junkies," there was little the plague doctors could do to stop the plague from spreading among them.

And all that the social planners, philosophers, and politicians did was point fingers at each other and spout their usual poppycock (how much that has remained the same, even with TeleCom). But there was another answer, an old and much-maligned one. Timothy, God is still the answer! May I never think I know so much that I know too little and so forget him. The master spoke to me many times through the words of Ephesians 5:15–21. Get your Bible now and read them again. You know any better plan? (I mean one that works better, not one that sounds better to a nascent techno-scientific egghead like you!)

Not sorry at all that I wrote that last true and fine sentence,

Uncle Luke

My Dear Timothy,

It was about time you wrote me back. It only took a hand-ful of letters from me to stir you up. Well, I must admit that I knew when I called you a nascent techno-scientific egghead that it might create some interest on your part in a bit of correspondence. It's about time! What do you think, I am writing you for my health? I've had enough trouble with this latest hip-lasering to keep me occupied enough. But instead I waste my crotchety time writing to you without reply!

What I meant by techno-scientific egghead was that there is more to the human body, heart, and soul than any of us has ever admitted. Who do we think we are? What proof is there that psalms and hymns and spiritual songs are not the answer? What proof is there that formulas and graphs and laboratories are the answer? Well, of course it depends on the question. But my question was not about the genetic map of the AIDS virus or the prevalence of Braindust use compared to intravenous heroin use. My question was, How can one really change the human heart and the human mind? How can one change behavior? How can we make the most of our time?

If you come up with a better answer than knowing Jesus Christ, let me know immediately by modem-alarm. If not, read all of Philippians 2. You will learn some of the quali-ties of the plague doctor there and you will receive some in-structions about the work you are to do. If you are to fol-low in my footsteps as a plague doctor, you will have to be a kindred spirit to me. And I have held fast the word of life, so that in the day of Christ I may have cause to glory; even me, because I did not run in vain nor toil in vain. This is the closest I will get to something like an apology. We both know your mother, my dear sister, was a believer and that your father, although I loved him, was an eggheaded technoscientist. Who was happier? Who was healthier? Whose philosophy makes for more caring and competent plague doctoring? I think you show initial signs of being your mother's son, my dear nephew. But like Paul, I must arrange to have some of your skin cut off every once in a while, even if I have to do it myself.

Acts 16:1–3,
Uncle Luke

My Dear Timothy:

Now I need to go back to medical history that is even older than I am. You might not think this possible, but I assure you loquaciousness is not the oldest disease.

Young plague doctors should know that AIDS is a disease with the stigma of leprosy, the transmission characteristics of syphilis, the natural history of tuberculosis, and the prognosis of the bubonic plague. I will divide this letter into readable sections based on these diseases. Sorry about the handwriting.

Leprosy

Leprosy remains endemic in a few parts of the world today, but its potential for epidemic has been checked by the discovery of effective treatment. The disease is caused by a mycobacterium, *Hansen's bacillus*. Leprosy is spread by direct skin-to-skin contact, nasal secretions, breast milk, and biting insects. The disease is not highly contagious, but children seem more susceptible than adults.

The clinical manifestations include skin sores, nerve deadening, and facial destruction. Leprosy is treatable. The epithet of "leper," however, still symbolizes social stigmatization. Christ touched stigmatized lepers; he was at some very small risk for contracting leprosy. Plague doctors who work with AIDS patients are at a very, very small risk for contracting AIDS. You know about the few cases in which health care workers contracted AIDS from accidentally puncturing themselves with a needle or from blood spattered in their eyes.

Many Christians, in light of Christ's example, overcame the stigma of leprosy and worked, hands-on, with lepers. I am one of those who overcame the stigma of AIDS and worked, hands-on, with AIDS patients. You will do the same.

Syphilis

Syphilis is a complex, sexually transmitted disease which can involve every organ system in the body if untreated. Syphilis caused great outbreaks in the past and remains a current but easily treated problem. The causative agent, *Treponema pallidum*, is exquisitely sensitive to ordinary penicillin and, unlike most other germs, has not developed resistance to this drug. The organism can only be transmitted sexually; it can't survive in the open air.

It has been known for centuries that syphilis can be avoided by mutually monogamous sexual relationships or the use of condoms during sexual activity. Because of its association with sexual activity outside of monogamous marriage, Christians have been far less sympathetic to syphilis patients than to leprosy patients. It was in the discussion about syphilis patients that the term *innocent victim* first emerged in the early 1900s and was used to describe children born with congenital syphilis or wives unknowingly infected by adulterous husbands.

Timothy, you must work this out for yourself: What degrees of innocence and guilt do victims have? I have no answer for you that can tell you all you need to know. There is something morally different in the cases of a promiscuous man or woman with AIDS and a child born to a mother who unknowingly contracted AIDS via her husband. Soldiers killed in battle are not victims, but civilians killed in battle are. It is a more difficult question than it first appears, and one I leave for you as a challenge.

Tuberculosis

Tuberculosis, or "consumption," was once a chronic, incurable disease which caused weight loss, wasting, and death among young people. Tuberculosis is now treatable. Tuberculosis is caused by a slow-growing organism, *Mycobacterium tuberculosis*, acquired by breathing in tiny infected droplets from the cough or sneeze of a person with T.B. Once the germ reaches the lung, it is engulfed by white blood cells, but survives and multiplies within them. In most cases the patient's white-cell defense system walls off the bacteria and the initial infection heals spontaneously. The bacilli remain alive, though dormant.

Active tuberculosis may develop decades later, when the patient's immune resistance is diminished and the still-living organisms are able to multiply. The incidence and prevalence of tuberculosis actually went up in the 1990s due to the AIDS epidemic and the lack of immune resistance many of our patients exhibited. The signs and symptoms of T.B. include fever, weight loss, cough, and skin lesions. Untreated, the natural history is one of slow progression; however, death is not inevitable. Chemotherapy is now so effective that most patients do not even require hospitalization.

Like leprosy patients, patients with tuberculosis were treated compassionately by the twentieth-century Christian community, which established sanitariums and provided resources for the care of the poor with T.B. We attempted to provide the same kinds of resources for the care of the poor with AIDS.

Bubonic Plague

Plague still occurs worldwide, and there are sporadic cases in the United States. The bubonic plague is caused by

Yersinia pestis, a bacteria which infects fleas, multiplies in their intestines, and blocks their digestive tracts. When the flea attempts to ingest blood it is forced to regurgitate the plague bacilli into the blood of its host. Patients develop lymph node swelling, nausea, vomiting, diarrhea, pneumonia, meningitis, and shock.

Untreated plague is remarkably deadly. In the three worldwide epidemics of bubonic plague (sixth, fourteenth, and nineteenth centuries A.D.), millions of people died. In later plagues, case fatality rates diminished, and it is possible that some people gradually developed some immunity to the bubonic plague.

A variety of common antibiotics are effective against the dreaded "black plague," but even treated with antibiotics, the case fatality rate is still nearly 50 percent. Fortunately, improved public and personal hygiene, made possible in many countries through the initial work of Christians, have made plague a rare disease in most parts of the world. Our challenge now, in the West, is to improve "social hygiene"— moral behavior—not mandated from without but coming forth from within. Timothy, remember what the master said about the tombs which looked good on the outside but are corrupted within.

The Plague of Plagues: AIDS

People with AIDS are as severely stigmatized as lepers, but AIDS sufferers evoke less compassion than leprosy patients because the transmission characteristics of AIDS are like those of syphilis. The tendency with both syphilis and AIDS is to assign blame or degrees of blame ("guilty" versus "somewhat guilty" or "innocent" victims). The natural plague time tendency to blame the victim is heightened in these two diseases. In the medieval plague times, the public tried to blame someone for the disease.

AIDS has the natural history of tuberculosis, with a long incubation period and a relatively slow, wasting course.

AIDS has the prognosis of untreated bubonic plague—nearly certain death. With the benefit of these comparisons, we can see why AIDS—a disease characterized by depressed immunity, a bewildering array of symptoms, several unusual cancers, and brain infection—is one of the most challenging plagues imaginable.

It is possible that in time, perhaps in several more generations, our immune systems will learn to fight the disease as the immune systems of some people probably learned to combat the bacillus of the bubonic plague. It is also possible that we will find a better vaccine for AIDS. Most AIDS researchers agree, however, that in the near future there is no reasonable hope for a completely effective vaccine, so our current vaccine will have to do.

As I said before, prevention is still the best medicine, Timothy, and I will talk a bit about prevention in my next letter. In the meantime, read about some of the plagues recorded for us in the Bible. Note that many seem to have been sent as a judgment. Is the plague of AIDS a judgment? I am not sure I know the answer. A lot depends on your own answer to my "innocent" versus "guilty" victim question. Would God plague us? Would he plague the innocent along with the guilty? You will have to arrive at your own conclusions. And don't forget to read John 9:1–12. Jesus wouldn't even discuss the question.

Exodus 32:35	2 Samuel 24:10–25
Numbers 11:33	Revelation 11:6
Numbers 14:37	Revelation 15:1, 6–8
Numbers 16:41–50	Revelation 16
Joshua 22:17	Revelation 22:18–19
1 Samuel 5:8–12	

Uncle Luke

My Dear Timothy,

Thank you for your recent letter. I am glad to see your

study of the biblical plagues yielded several important principles which you so thoughtfully outlined. l agree that God
can use plague as judgment if he will, and also that some of
the plagues seemed potentially explainable from what we
know of infectious diseases. I also agree that Jesus did not
attribute disease to God's doing, but rather attributed healing to his glory. Good work, nephew! Keep it up.

Let me share with you some of the ideas for prevention
of AIDS that were prevalent in the 1990s, and then my own
idea based on Numbers 16. First, you should realize that the
risk of AIDS from blood transfusion was virtually elimi-
nated by 1985, when the ELISA test for antibody to the
AIDS virus became available. Since then, AIDS has not been
a major problem in the blood supply of the United States,
since all blood products in every blood bank here are either
tested for AIDS or treated in a manner which results in the
destruction of the HIV. However, since false negative tests
are still a potential problem, especially in the early phase of
the disease (the first three months after contact), and since
a person's own blood is always the safest, we usually told
patients having elective surgery that it would be wise to bank
their own blood. Now we use Artifblood.

Throughout the 1990s, AIDS was a major problem in the
blood banks of the third world. Tests on units of blood from
Kenya in 1986 showed that as many as one in six units was
contaminated by AIDS. The nonsexual transmission of AIDS
through contaminated units of blood, syringes and other
equipment was a medical hazard in many countries, and
many thousands of people in these areas were unknowingly
infected with AIDS. As I mentioned earlier, the cost of screening donated blood was prohibitive in these countries.

Medical science told us that AIDS could best be avoided
by mutual monogamy. Less sure methods of avoiding AIDS
were said to be noninsertive sexual relations or the use of
condoms during insertive sexual relations. Data from 1994

indicated that condoms were not as "safe" as was initially predicted, and several authorities suggested that condoms were often ineffective during anal sex. Male homosexuals were forced to change many of their practices.

We also know that needle-borne transmission could be prevented by not using drugs, or if drugs were used, by not sharing needles and syringes. Some politicians proposed handing out free needles. I always wondered when they would propose handing out free drugs. We are almost there today, with the widespread use of Braindust. I don't trust the stuff. Don't you ever use it! Talk about an opiate of the poor!

We tried to minimize perinatal transmission by testing high-risk women for AIDS. If a woman had the virus, we told her that she had a 30 to 50 percent chance of transmitting it to her unborn baby.

The scientific model tried to tell us how to prevent the transmission of AIDS; it worked better in preventing some aspects of transmission than in others. For example, the problem of making the blood supply safe was not predominantly a moral one, it was a technical and financial one, requiring the application of a laboratory test to every unit of blood.

But in the area of sexual transmission, AIDS, like syphilis, caused and continues to cause some conflict between the scientific community and the religious communities. Science would prevent transmission primarily by Impermoconds; religious morality would prevent transmission primarily by premarital chastity and marital monogamy. Finding common ground was difficult in syphilis and was difficult in AIDS as well.

How should we approach the prevention of AIDS? Is science wrong and the religious sexual morality right, or vice versa? Is their conflict irreconcilable? Who won then and who's winning now?

Timothy, you need to construct a scorecard, using information from prior plagues as well as the current one. How have Christians done in the past plagues, and how have we done with the latest one?

Historically, regarding the choices to desert, persecute, or show compassion to plague victims, Christians have put in a mixed performance at best. On a disease-by-disease basis, we have done somewhat better with leprosy, tuberculosis, and some outbreaks of bubonic plague than we have done with syphilis. In AIDS, as in syphilis, we have been fairly quick to abandon, assess blame, and persecute the victims.

As in other plagues, however, there were notable and praiseworthy exceptions. Christians like Dr. Daniel Moreschi started AIDS clinics in several cities. Christian journalists like Ben Patterson urged us to remember that there is mercy and forgiveness with God, and that it is our job to give AIDS victims hope in this mercy and forgiveness. Many Christians, like your correspondent, quietly cared for AIDS patients in a variety of practical ways. But the tendency to desert, blame, and persecute has remained a strong, even predominant, influence.

Now that we have chastised the church, let's take an equally critical look at the scorecard for the scientific model. Regarding desertion, blame, or persecution: generally good marks. But regarding ability to prevent AIDS thus far: very poor marks. Offering education and condoms for prevention of sexually transmitted diseases (STDs) didn't work well for syphilis and gonorrhea and worked only a little better for AIDS. Millions of people continue to get AIDS.

As Dr. Joe S. McIlhaney pointed out in the CMDS *Journal* fifty years ago, the only sure way of preventing STD, and the only real answer to the problem, is to educate our patients that what Scripture has been teaching for thousands of years remains true. If sex is avoided until marriage, and then engaged in only in marriage, STDs can be avoided. So the church gets high marks for speaking a difficult truth that society doesn't want to hear. And the evidence bore out this truth: the risk of AIDS was directly related to the number of lifelong sexual partners, especially if any of these partners shared needles.

The quandary that plague doctors face is that sexual behavior results in medical problems but is not itself a controllable medical variable. When physicians are forced by a disease like AIDS to try to intervene in the area of sexual behavior, they move outside the domain where the scientific model works to its fullest. While we may be able to be of some help (and like Dr. McIlhaney, I thought we ought to counsel patients accordingly), matters of morality are actually decided in broader provinces than medicine: home, school, and church. When it comes to controlling sexual behavior, conscience is stronger than data about disease. Sex is a powerful drive, after all.

Do you remember hearing about a lady named Dr. Ruth? She kept saying AIDS was bad and sex was good, but she was never very clear about the context in which sex was good. Her style of good sex could lead to a bad case of AIDS, especially if her followers forgot to use condoms (and I can testify that they often did).

Timothy, the hour is late and my hand is tired. Old people do run on so. I will have to wait until next time to tell you of another method for preventing the plague which I learned from Aaron. Remember always my love and concern for you, the young plague doctor who will soon follow after me.

Romans 16:25–27,

Uncle Luke

My Dear Timothy,

Another way to stop plague is by using an approach which worked once for Aaron. It requires that Christians use their own bodies to stop plague; it requires that we actually practice chastity and monogamy as a means of arresting the plague. Since the plague is largely sexually transmitted,

Christians can be the living barrier—better than any latex barrier—between the living and the dying. The biblical story which illustrates this approach describes a scene in which Aaron himself was a barrier to the plague.

> And Moses said unto Aaron, "Take a censer, and put fire therein from off the altar, and put on incense, and go quickly into the congregation, and make an atonement for them: for there is wrath gone out from the LORD; the plague is begun."
>
> And Aaron took as Moses commanded, and ran into the midst of the congregation; and behold, the plague was begun among the people; and he put on incense, and made an atonement for the people.
>
> And he stood between the dead and the living; and the plague was stayed (Num. 16:46–48 KJV).

One way for the plague of AIDS to be stopped is for Christians who propose chastity to be chaste, and for those who advocate monogamy to be monogamous—they and their families acting as a living barrier. From what we know of the AIDS plague, the rapid spread throughout the population would stop if enough people acted as living barriers to the virus. While standing between the dying and living, Christians are to pray for God's grace upon the world and for the plague to be stayed.

Of course, individual members of the barrier, like Aaron, are prone to sin and failing, so the barrier will be imperfect and incomplete. The living barrier approach, like the other approaches, is not totally effective. But it would slow the spread of plague and limit its progress.

Some might say the living barrier approach is simply a matter of Christians "practicing what they preach." In some ways it is. The transmission characteristics of AIDS, however, combined with the dramatic scene of Aaron standing between the living and the dead, make this a unique and fundamentally effective approach even if not a word is "preached" by those who employ it. Avoiding sex is a quiet activity. More than moralisms or condoms, our bodies have the final and complete clinical power against the sexual transmission of this disease.

In the conflict between the scientific approach and the moralistic approach to AIDS prevention, the living barrier may make sense to both groups, because it can be both scientifically successful and morally voluntary.

What do you think?

2 Timothy 3:14–27,
Uncle Luke

My Dear Timothy:

Writing these letters has made me fatigued in a peculiar sort of way. It is almost as if I am pouring out all I have seen and known of plague, in a disorganized and staccato fashion, to be sure. But still it is my life's work and thought. How can I help you to care for plague patients and to think about the prevention and treatment of such a complex plague as AIDS? I am glad you sent me your notes on the content of Aaron's prayer. They made me feel my time spent in drafting these letters has been worthwhile.

I think this will be my final letter. My hip-lasering hurts more and more each day and I feel that the master will call me soon. You know my age. I can scarcely believe that I could live to be this old. I remember when I first accepted Christ, at age four, my mother told the whole family that since we were all Christians, whoever got to heaven first should wait for the rest of us; we would all be together there soon enough. But even though your dear mother is there, and the rest of my family, I am still the earthly holdout. And after all I have faced! In losing my life I must have gained it back again. There is no other good explanation. My only tips to you are to drink skim milk and never eat the yolk of an egg. In your letter you mentioned some of the things you eat. They sound horrible.

In plague time, many physicians choose not to care for plague patients. I have chosen to follow Christ in both his treatment of the blind man and lepers and his handling of the woman caught in adultery. In a way, the AIDS plague calls for both responses at once. That's why it is so difficult for us to understand how to deal with AIDS.

You know how proud I am of you. You have chosen to become a plague doctor in a very difficult time. There are so many patients. Money is always a problem. The politics are complex. But I know you will try to follow the example of the master who is the great physician. And remember me. I am beloved of many patients; some of these I will see in heaven. If I do not write again it is not because I have forgotten about you. I have seen enough of the plague. Look for me next where there is no sickness.

Revelation 21:1–4,
Uncle Luke

18

Flimsy Costumes

My white coat hangs in the hall closet, its fraying pockets filled by my stethoscope, reflex hammer, pen light, alcohol wipes, tourniquets, and several small medical texts. Above the left breast pocket my name is embroidered in red, matching the nearby drops of blood that peroxide hasn't removed. The buttons are imitation pearl. The coat is cut long, but the sleeves are perhaps an inch too short.

This is my health professional's coat, and I have earned it and worn it this last decade. Hanging in the closet, arms folded limply, it waits for an infusion of flesh and life. I have discovered only recently that it is just a doctor costume, and like all costumes, is flimsy, temporary, and useful only on certain occasions.

Once, when I was caring for a young child with an inherited disease that causes brittle bones and kidney failure from calcium deposits in the kidneys, my white coat got in the way. The boy had been operated on by physicians in white coats; his blood had been drawn by venipuncturists in white coats; an occasional urinary catheterization had been performed by nurses in white coats.

So, all of us who wanted to be close to him took off our coats and hung them by the nurses' station and walked into his room without our costumes. It was odd how bare I felt when I did this, without the familiar weights of my hammer and pen light and texts, stethoscope hidden discreetly in my pocket. Day after day I visited without the coat, talking with William and his family.

What I lost in authority or efficiency (I had to scramble around looking for alcohol wipes and tourniquets) I gained in closeness. William talked about his impending death, his expectations of heaven, his view of God.

Each time I left the room and put on the white coat it seemed a little heavier, its pockets bulkier, its clinking and clattering instruments more intrusive.

Then there was James, the AIDS patient suffering from multiple infections. He was losing weight and vigor daily despite our treatments, visibly dying in our modern, state-of-the-art hospital despite all the expertise my coat could bring. Daily I heard the rhonchi (rattles in his breathing) with my stethoscope; my pocket medical books and recent journal articles gave treatment protocols which helped but did not cure.

The coat proved little more than an old-fashioned white shirt against this disease. Temporary and dated, it held no power of treatment, no innate ability to cure. I sat helplessly on its long tail at the side of James's bed and watched him dwindle.

I should have known the coat was temporary when Janet, age seventeen, was admitted to the emergency room after collapsing at home. I ran to her bed, coat flying behind, and we began the response to emergencies that we call The Code. I had difficulty intubating her because of all the vomit in her airway—pizza—but succeeded on the second try. Someone was doing chest compressions, and I found the central line tray and inserted the large needle into her jugular vein. We worked for an hour without success.

They rolled her down the hall, and I looked at my coat, covered with vomit and blood, a pocket torn by the handles of the bed frame.

I wore the coat at first under an illusion of physical immortality. It was my shield; it covered my vulnerability, my soft underbelly filled with the destructible organs I worried about during my sophomore year in medical school. I thought my patients would be older than me, would die in nursing homes, would slip gently away.

Then I saw William, met James, lost Janet. I noted occasional chest pains, had back stiffness, and got tendonitis of my shoulder after waxing my car. I seriously considered a diet, reconsidered exercise, became older than half my father's age.

I am now old enough to be in the early risk group for a heart attack. I notice cemeteries, and I am more careful when driving or dangling from ladders.

Underneath my flimsy costume, my temporary uniform, my dress whites, I see a human body, intricate but prone to disease, adaptable but aging. The physician's humanity cannot be covered for long by name tags, instruments, pocket texts, and white cloth.

My personal fragility links me to you, and you to me. All of our costumes are flimsy and temporary, for there comes a day, sooner or later, when they will hang empty in hall closets. When our beliefs will be tested. When we will determine if there is a resurrection of the body and a life everlasting.

Each of us will have a turn. My turn will remind you, and yours will remind me, of what we always and finally have in common.

Notes

Chapter 3: Honor Thy Patient

1. Schloendorff vs. Society of New York Hospital, 211 N.Y. 125, 105 N.E. 92, 95 (1914).

2. W. L. Prosser, *Handbook of the Law of Torts*, 4th ed. (St. Paul: West Publishing Company, 1971), #10 at 36, #32 at 165, cited in *President's Commission for the Study of Ethical Problems in Medicine and Biomedical and Behavioral Research*, Vol. 1:20–1.

3. Ibid.: 28.

4. Ibid.: 31.

5. J. Katz, *The Silent World of Doctor and Patient* (New York: Free Press, 1984), See also Jay Katz, "Disclosure and Consent: In Search of Their Roots," in *Genetics and the Law II*, eds. Aubrey Milansky and George J. Annas (New York: Plenum Press, 1980):124.

6. L. Kass, "Ethical Dilemmas in the Care of the Ill: What Is the Physician's Service?" *Journal of the American Medical Association* 244 (1980):1811–16.

7. R. C. Sider and C. D. Clements, "The New Medical Ethics: A Second Opinion," *Archives of Internal Medicine* 145 (1985):2169–71.

8. J. Katz, *The Silent World*:20.

9. S. E. Bedell and T. L. Delbanco, "Choices about Cardiopulmonary Resuscitation in the Hospital: When Do Physicians Talk to Patients?" *New England Journal of Medicine* 310 (1984):1089–93.

10. M. Angell, "Respecting the Autonomy of Competent Patients," ibid.:1115–16.

11. M. Siegler, "Searching for Moral Certainty in Medicine: A Proposal for a New Model of the Doctor-Patient Encounter," *Bulletin of the New York Academy of Medicine* 57 (1981):56–69.

12. L. Emanuel. "Advance Directives: What Have We Learned So Far?" *The Journal of Clinical Ethics*, 4(1993):8–16.

Chapter 4: Shared Prayer

1. T. Merton, *Contemplative Prayer* (New York: Doubleday, 1971):67.

2. A. W. Tozer, *The Pursuit of God* (Harrisburg, PA: Christian Publications, Inc., 1948):15.

Chapter 6: High Technology Medicine

1. S. J. Youngner, C. Coulton, R. Welton, B. Juknialis, D. L. Jackson, "ICU Visiting Policies," *Critical Care Medicine* 12 (1984):606–8.

2. J. E. Frader, "Difficulties in Providing Intensive Care," *Pediatrics* 64 (1979):10–16.

3. G. D. Phillips, "Life Support Systems in Intensive Care: A Review of History, Ethics, Cost, Benefit, and Rational Use," *Anaesthesia and Intensive Care* 5 (1977):2517.

4. J. Ellul, *The Technological Society* (New York: Knopf, 1964).

5. L. J. Schneiderman, R. M. Kaplan, R. A. Pearlman, H. Teetzel, "Do Physicians' Own Preferences for Life-Sustaining Treatment Influence Their Perceptions of Patients' Preferences?" *The Journal of Clinical Ethics,* 4(1993):28–33.

Chapter 7: Treating "Gomers"

1. Samuel Shem. *The House of God.* (New York: Dell, 1981).

Chapter 9: When CPR Becomes Futile

1. L. J. Schneiderman, N. S. Jecker, A. R. Jonsen, "Medical Futility: Its Meaning and Ethical Implications," *Annals of Internal Medicine* 112 (1990):949–54.

2. N. S. Jecker, L. J. Schneiderman, "An Ethical Analysis of the Use of 'Futility' in the 1992 American Heart Association Guidelines for CPR and Emergency Cardiac Care," *Archives of Internal Medicine* 153 (1993):2195–98.

3. S. E. Bedell, T. L. Delbanco, E. F. Cook, F. H. Epstein, "Survival after Cardiopulmonary Resuscitation in the Hospital," *New England Journal of Medicine* 309 (1983):569–576; M. Gordon, E. Hurowitz, "Cardiopulmonary Resuscitation of the Elderly," *Journal of American Geriatric Society* 32 (1984):930–4; U. S. Congress, Johnson, P. H. Tanser, R. A. Ulan, T. E. Wood, "Results of Cardiac Resuscitation in 552 patients," *American Journal of Cardiology* 20 (1967):831–5.

4. S. J. Youngner, "Do-Not-Resuscitate Orders: No Longer Secret, but Still a Problem," *Hastings Center Report* 17 (1987):24–33.

5. G. E. Taffet, T. A. Teasdale, R. J. Luchi, "In-Hospital Cardiopulmonary Resuscitation," *JAMA* 260 (1988):2069–72. Also M. Rosenberg, C. Wang, S. Hoffman Wilde, D. Hickman, "Results of CPR Failure to Predict Survival in two Community Hospitals," *Archives of Internal Medicine* 153(1993):1370–75.

6. D. J. Murphy, "Do-Not-Resuscitate Orders: Time for Reappraisal in Long-Term-Care Institutions," *JAMA* 260 (1988):2098–2101.

7. U. S. Congress, Office of Technology Assessment, *Life-Sustaining Technologies and the Elderly*, OTA-BA–306 (Washington, D.C.: U.S. Government Printing Office, July 1987): 167–201.

8. J. E. Ruark, T. A. Raffin, and the Stanford University Medical Center Committee on Ethics, "Initiating and Withdrawing Life Support: Principles and Practice in Adult Medicine," *New England Journal of Medicine* 318 (1988):25–30.

Chapter 10: In Due Season

1. E. D. Pellegrino, "Educating the Humanist Physician: An Ancient Ideal Reconsidered," *Journal of the American Medical Association* 227 (1974):1288–94.

2. L. Kass, *Toward a More Natural Science*, (New York: The Free Press, 1985), p. 234.

3. S. H. Wanzer, S. J. Adelstein, R. E. Cranford, et al., "The Physician's Responsibility Toward Hopelessly Ill Patients: A Second Look," *New England Journal of Medicine* 320 (1989):844–49.

Chapter 11: In the Valley of the Shadow

1. B. Jennett, F. Plum, "Persistent Vegetative State After Brain Damage: A Syndrome in Search of a Name," *The Lancet* 1 (April, 1971):734–7.

2. P. Ramsey, *Ethics at the Edges of Life* (New Haven: Yale University Press, 1978):14.

3. A. R. Jonsen, M. Siegler, W. J. Winslade, *Clinical Ethics*, 3d ed. (New York: McGraw Hill, Macmillan, 1992).

4. E. Payne, "The Nancy Beth Cruzan Case," *Biblical Reflections on Modern Medicine* 1 (January, 1990):1–2.

Chapter 12: Cadaver Ethics

1. L. Kass, "Thinking About the Body." Hastings Center Report, February 1985:20–30.

2. R. Selzer, "The Corpse." *Mortal Lessons: Notes on the Art of Surgery* (New York: Simon and Schuster, 1974):1356.

3. *Science* 1978; 199:1420.

Chapter 13: The Call to Serve

1. L. S. King, "Medicine: Trade or Profession," *Journal of American Medical Association* 253 (1985):2709–10.

2. C. O. Dummett, "Bioethics and History: Neglected Essentials of Modern Dentistry," *Compendium of Continuing Education in Dentistry* 7 (1986):230–8.

3. M. G. Kramer, "Professionalism and the Principles of Ethics: Changing Concepts in Dentistry," *Pediatric Dentistry* 2 (1980):245–51.

4. E. D. Pelligrino, "Educating the Christian Doctor," *CMDS Study Guide,* 1989.

5. H. Habecker, "CMDS in Focus," *CMDS Journal* 21, no. 3 (1990):31.

6. M. Siegler, D. L. Schiedermayer, "Clinical Dental Ethics: Defining an Ethic for Practicing Professionals," *Journal of American College of Dentistry* 55 (1988):4–8.

Chapter 14: A Special Love for Gold

1. A. M. Angell, "How Much Will Health Care Reform Cost?" *New England Journal of Medicine,* 328 (1993):1778–9.

2. L. J. Morse, "A Declaration of Independence for Health System Reform," *New England Journal of Medicine* 329(1993):804–5.

3. I. Muller, "The Professional Ethics of the Greek Physician," *Bulletin of the History of Medicine* 30 (1956):391–419.

4. J. Fleetwood, "Some Lesser Known Irish Physicians," address to the Osler Club of London, May 1981.

5. T. Perry, Jr., "Surgery in a Rural Area: 1638–1868," *The American Journal of Surgery* 129 (1975):347–55.

6. R. S. Agnes, "Physician's Fees, 1856–2056," *New England Journal of Medicine* 290 (1974):751–2.

7. E. Ginzberg, "What Lies Ahead for American Physicians: One Economist's Views," *Journal of the American Medical Association* 253 (1985):2848–9.

Chapter 15: Medical Economics and the Free-Lunch Syndrome

1. "Opren Scandal," (Editorial), *The Lancet* (January 29, 1983): 219–20.

2. D. M. Musher, E. J. Young, R. J. Hamill, "The Ethics of Pharmaceutical Promotion," *New England Journal of Medicine* (August 28, 1986):590.

3. K. Millwe, W. A. Gouveia, M. Barza, et. al., "Undesirable Marketing Practices in the Pharmaceutical Industry," *New England Journal of Medicine* (July 4, 1985):54.

4. J. Graves, "Frequent Flyer Programs for Drug Prescribing," *New England Journal of Medicine* (July 23, 1987):252.

5. M. A. Jenke, "Relations Between Physicians and Pharmaceutical Companies: Where to Draw the Line," *New England Journal of Medicine* (Feb. 2, 1990):557.

6. D. L. Schiedermayer, W. P. McKinney, "The Feldene Connection: Drug Dealing in the Doctor's Parking Lot?" *New England Journal of Medicine* (November 10, 1988):718.

7. D. A. Kessler, W. L. Pines, "The Federal Regulation of Prescription Drug Advertising and Promotion," *Journal of American Medical Association* 264 (1990):2409–15.

8. W. P. McKinney, D. L. Schiedermayer, N. Lurie, "Attitudes of Internal Medicine Faculty and Residents Toward Professional Interaction with Pharmaceutical Sales Representatives, *Journal of American Medical Association* 264 (Oct. 3, 1990):1693–7.

9. Royal College of Physicians, "The Relationship Between Physicians and the Pharmaceutical Industry, *Journal of Royal College of Physicians* 20 (1986):235–42.

10. American College of Physicians, "Physicians and the Pharmaceutical Industry," *Annals of Internal Medicine* 112 (1990):624–26.

Suggested Readings

Beauchamp, T. L. and J. F. Childress. *Principles of Biomedical Ethics*. 3d ed. New York: Oxford University Press, 1991.
Excellent discussion of the various principles and theories of ethics.

Beckwith, F. and N. L. Geisler. *Matters of Life and Death: Calm Answers to Tough Questions about Abortion and Euthanasia*. Grand Rapids: Baker Books, 1993.
A multidisciplinary approach to medicine, science, ethics, philosophy, and theology to prepare thoughtful, reasonable responses to tough and echnical questions arising from the right-to-life issues.

Biebel, David B. *How to Help a Heartbroken Friend: What to Do and What to Say When a Friend Is Going Through Tough Times*. Nashville: Thomas Nelson, 1993.
Practical suggestions on how to help rather than hurt those who are suffering. The book's guidelines reflect the author's experience with grief and suffering.

Callahan, D. *Setting Limits: Medical Goals in an Aging Society*. New York: Simon and Schuster, 1987.
Callahan raises important questions about our medical goals in an aging population. He is basically against active euthanasia of the elderly.

Davis, John J. *Evangelical Ethics*. Phillipsburg, N.J.: Presbyterian and Reformed, 1985.
The author discusses abortion, reproductive technologies, and a number of other clinical issues. The book is well written and well referenced and is a good source of background information.

Jones, D. C. *Biblical Christian Ethics*. Grand Rapids: Baker, 1994.
Introductory survey approaches ethics as the "study of the way of life that conforms to the will of God." In examining issues and dilemmas, ethical systems are explained and Scripture's teachings are stressed.

Jonsen, A. R., M. Siegler, and W. J. Winslade. *Clinical Ethics: A Practical Approach to Ethical Decisions in Clinical Medicine*. 3d ed. New York: McGraw-Hill, 1992.
Short, readable, discussion of clinical ethics. Case studies of informed consent, treatment refusal, do-not-resuscitate orders, etc., make this an important and practical book.

Kass, L. R. *Toward a More Natural Science: Biology and Human Affairs.*
New York: The Free Press, 1985.
   Kass is concerned about the doctor-patient relationship. His thought-
ful analysis of the meaning of the Hippocratic Oath is eloquent.

Lammers, S. E. and A. Verhey. *On Moral Medicine: Theological Perspectives in Medical Ethics.* Grand Rapids: W. B. Eerdmans, 1987.
   A wide-ranging collection of ethics codes and essays from authors
as diverse as C. S. Lewis and Ivan Illich. A good reference volume.

La Puma, J. and D. Schiedermayer. *Ethics Consultation: A Practical
Guide.* Boston: Jones and Barlett, 1994.
   Addresses the clinical method of ethics case consultation from beginning the consult to calling family meetings and writing a report.
Also considers issues of training, skills, and certification for ethics
consultants and ethics committees. The appendix contains twenty-five
actual consults and their resolutions.

Orr, R. D., D. Schiedermayer and D. B. Biebel. *Life and Death Decisions:
Help in Making Tough Choices about Bioethical Issues.* Colorado
Springs: Navpress, 1990.
   A survey of a number of general ethics issues. The book is intended
for use in the adult Christian education format. Small group discus-
sion questions are included.

Ramsey, P. *The Patient as Person.* New Haven: Yale University Press,
1970.
———. *Ethics at the Edges of Life.* New Haven: Yale University Press,
1978.
   The ethicist and theologian Paul Ramsey was the most consistent
and intellectually formidable proponent of the sanctity of life principle. He strongly outlines and defends this principle in both of these
books.

Spring, B. and E. Larson. *Euthanasia: Spiritual, Medical, and Legal Issues in Terminal Health Care.* Portland: Multnomah Press, 1988.
   A short, interesting, and well-researched book which explores the
legal trends in health care, the views of leading ethicists and theo-
logians, and historical Christian responses to euthanasia. Surrogacy,
decision-making, living wills, and hospice care are also discussed.

Glossary

acute sudden, severe, of short duration as differentiated from chronic

anoxia deprivation of adequate oxygen

anoxic encephalopathy brain dysfunction due to damage through lack of oxygen

arterial cutdown surgical procedure to locate artery for purpose of administering fluids

asystole cessation of heart contractions

autonomy self-determination

beneficence doing good

bradycardia abnormally slow heartbeat

cardiomyopathy diseased heart muscle

cardioversions electric shocks administered to heart to restore regular rhythm

clinical having to do with health professionals' practice

clinical ethics pertaining to the principles, virtues, values, and moral decision-making practices in hospitals, clinics, and offices

code cardiopulmonary resuscitation (CPR) performed during cardiac arrest

code team doctors, nurses, and other health professionals on-call to perform codes

coma unarousable; unresponsiveness as a result of injury or illness

competency presumed ability of adults to make a variety of decisions

cortex outer layer of brain; gray matter

decision-making capacity the patient's ability to make medical decisions; decisional

defibrillation shocking a fibrillating heart by an electronic device to return it to a normal sinus rhythm

edema accumulation of excessive water in tissues; swelling

enteral given through mouth; by way of the intestines

febrile having fever

fidelity faithfulness

flaccid no muscle tone

hypotensive having low blood pressure

hypoxic deprived of adequate oxygen in lungs and blood

impotent the inability of a man to have an erection

myocardial infarction damage to heart wall, or muscle, as a result of deprivation of blood supply

myocardium heart muscle; heart wall

191

necrotic tissue (necrosis)   dead tissue (dying tissue)

no code   the decision to forego resuscitation; DNR

osteomyelitis   infection of the bone

parenteral   given by injection into the vein

patent ductus arteriosus   in a fetus a blood vessel that connects the lung artery and the heart (aorta), normally closed by birth and therefore abnormal if open (patent); is treatable

pleura   lining of chest cavity; covering of the lungs

pleural effusion   fluid in the pleural space

pleural sclerosis   thickening or hardening of the pleural layers

retinopathy   diseased retina (inner layer of eye)

sepsis (septic)   illness or condition caused by bacteria in the bloodstream

sinus tachycardia   rapid, but not life-threatening, increase in heart rate

Swan Ganz catheter   catheter inserted into a large chest vein and advanced to heart's main artery leading to lungs. The instrument measures pulmonary arterial pressure.

vascularization   formation of new blood vessels

ventricular fibrillation   uncoordinated muscle activity of the ventricles; precedes asytole

ventricular tachycardia   abnormally rapid heartbeat, originating in a ventricle, often life-threatening

veracity   truth-telling